Calculus

ELEVENTH EDITION

Ron Larson
The Pennsylvania State University, The Behrend College

Bruce Edwards
University of Florida

Prepared by

Ron Larson
The Pennsylvania State University, The Behrend College

CENGAGE
Learning·

Australia · Brazil · Mexico · Singapore · United Kingdom · United States

National Geographic Learning/Cengage Learning is pleased to offer our college-level materials to high schools for Advanced Placement®, honors, and electives courses. To contact your National Geographic Learning representative, please call us toll-free at **1-888-915-3276** or visit us at **http://ngl.cengage.com**.

For permission to use material from this text or product, submit all requests online at **www.cengage.com/permissions** Further permissions questions can be emailed to **permissionrequest@cengage.com**.

ISBN: 978-1-337-28700-5

Cengage Learning
20 Channel Center Street
Boston, MA 02210
USA

Cengage Learning is a leading provider of customized learning solutions with office locations around the globe, including Singapore, the United Kingdom, Australia, Mexico, Brazil, and Japan. Locate your local office at: **www.cengage.com/global**.

Cengage Learning products are represented in Canada by Nelson Education, Ltd.

To learn more about Cengage Learning Solutions, visit **www.cengage.com**.

To find online supplements and other instructional support, please visit **www.cengagebrain.com**.

AP® is a trademark registered and/or owned by the College Board, which was not involved in the production of, and does not endorse, this product.

Printed in the United States of America
Print Number: 01   Print Year: 2017

Chapter P   Preparation for Calculus

Chapter Comments

Chapter P is a review chapter and, therefore, should be covered quickly. Spend about 3 or 4 days on this chapter, placing most of the emphasis on Section P.3. Of course, you cannot cover every single item that is in this chapter in that time, so this is a good opportunity to encourage your students to read the book. To convince your students of this, assign homework problems or give a quiz on some of the material that is in this chapter but that you do not go over in class. Although you will not hold your students responsible for everything in all 16 chapters, the tools in this chapter need to be readily at hand, that is, memorized.

Sections P.1 and P.2 can be covered in a day. Students at this level of mathematics have graphed equations before so let them read about that information on their own. Discuss intercepts, emphasizing that they are points, not numbers, and, so, should be written as ordered pairs. Also discuss symmetry with respect to the x-axis, the y-axis, and the origin. Be sure to do a problem like Example 5 in Section P.1. Students need to be able to find the points of intersection of graphs in order to calculate the area between two curves in Chapter 7.

In Section P.2, discuss the slope of a line, the point-slope form of a line, equations of vertical and horizontal lines, and the slopes of parallel and perpendicular lines. You need to emphasize the point-slope form of a line because this is needed to write the equation of a tangent line in Chapter 2.

Students need to know everything in Section P.3, so carefully go over the definition of a function, domain and range, function notation, transformations, the terms algebraic and transcendental, and the composition of functions. Note that the authors assume a knowledge of trigonometric functions. If necessary to review these functions, refer to Appendix C. Because students need practice handling Δx, be sure to do an example calculating $f(x + \Delta x)$. Your students should know the graphs of the eight basic functions in Figure P.27. A knowledge of even and odd functions will be helpful with definite integrals.

Section P.4 provides students with a comprehensive review of the fundamentals of trigonometry. The section presents the six trigonometric functions along with their domains, ranges, how to find values, and graphing, and develops a list of important properties. Uses of right triangles, circles, and the standard unit circle are presented.

The authors assume students have a working knowledge of inequalities, the formula for the distance between two points, absolute value, and so forth. If needed, you can find a review of these concepts in Appendix C.

Section P.1   Graphs and Models

Section Comments

P.1   **Graphs and Models**—Sketch the graph of an equation. Find the intercepts of a graph. Test a graph for symmetry with respect to an axis and the origin. Find the points of intersection of two graphs. Interpret mathematical models for real-life data.

Teaching Tips

You may want to spend time reviewing factoring, solving equations involving square roots, and solving polynomial equations. For further review, encourage students to study the following material in *Precalculus*, 10th edition, by Larson.

- Factoring: Appendix A.3

- Solving equations involving square roots: Appendix A.5

- Solving polynomial equations: Appendix A.5

1

Encourage students who have access to a graphing utility or computer algebra system to use the technology to check their answers.

Start class by having students practice finding intercepts of the graph of an equation. Consider doing an in class example of finding the intercepts of the graph of an equation with a radical, such as $y = \sqrt{x + 4}$ or $y = x\sqrt{4 - x^2}$.

Students have a hard time deciding if certain graphs are symmetric to the x-axis, y-axis, and origin. To help their understanding, tell students that the word *symmetric* conveys balance. If you want to set a dinner table, you want to have matching plates, utensils, and everything in line. To further aid students' understanding of symmetry, draw pictures of various symmetries. Suggested examples are shown below:

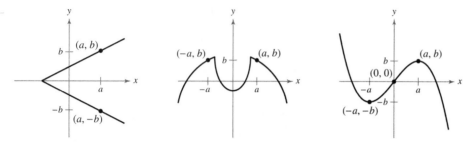

When finding points of intersection, it is useful to have students find the points both algebraically and by using a graphing calculator. Use Example 5 on page 6 to find the points of intersection using a graphing utility.

How Do You See It? Exercise

Page 9, Exercise 74 Use the graphs of the two equations to answer the questions below.

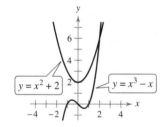

(a) What are the intercepts for each equation?

(b) Determine the symmetry for each equation.

(c) Determine the point of intersection of the two equations.

Solution

(a) Intercepts for $y = x^3 - x$:

y-intercept: $y = 0^3 - 0 = 0$; $(0, 0)$

x-intercepts: $0 = x^3 - x = x(x^2 - 1) = x(x - 1)(x + 1)$; $(0, 0), (1, 0), (-1, 0)$

Intercepts for $y = x^2 + 2$:

y-intercept: $y = 0 + 2 = 2$; $(0, 2)$

x-intercepts: $0 = x^2 + 2$

None, y cannot equal 0.

2

(b) Symmetry with respect to the origin for $y = x^3 - x$ because

$$-y = (-x)^3 - (-x) = -x^3 + x.$$

Symmetry with respect to the y-axis for $y = x^2 + 2$ because

$$y = (-x)^2 + 2 = x^2 + 2.$$

(c)
$$x^3 - x = x^2 + 2$$

$$x^3 - x^2 - x - 2 = 0$$

$$(x - 2)(x^2 + x + 1) = 0$$

$$x = 2 \implies y = 6$$

Point of intersection: $(2, 6)$

Note: The polynomial $x^2 + x + 1$ has no real roots.

Suggested Homework Assignment

Pages 8–9: 1–15 odd, 19–55 odd, 65, and 67.

Section P.2   Linear Models and Rates of Change

Section Comments

P.2   **Linear Models and Rates of Change**—Find the slope of a line passing through two points. Write the equation of a line with a given point and slope. Interpret slope as a ratio or as a rate in a real-life application. Sketch the graph of a linear equation in slope-intercept form. Write equations of lines that are parallel or perpendicular to a given line.

Teaching Tips

Spend time reviewing the following concepts: slope, writing equations of lines, and slope as a rate of change. For further review, encourage students to study the following material in *Precalculus*, 10th edition, by Larson.

- Slope: Section 1.3

- Finding the slope of a line: Section 1.3

- Writing linear equations in two variables: Section 1.3

- Parallel and perpendicular lines: Section 1.3

- Slope as a rate of change: Section 1.3

Encourage students who have access to a graphing utility or computer algebra system to use the technology to check their answers.

Review with the class that slope measures the steepness of a line. In addition, the slope of a line is a rate of change. Rate of change is an important topic in calculus, and inform students that rate of change will come up later in the semester.

Consider doing an example in class to remind students how to rewrite an equation such as $x + 3y = 12$ in slope-intercept form. Then show them how to identify the slope and y-intercept. Remind students that the slope of a vertical line is undefined and the slope of a horizontal line is 0. (As mentioned before, you can also direct students to the appropriate material in *Precalculus*.)

3

When finding equations of lines, be sure to write each solution in four ways: slope-intercept form, two equations in point-slope form (depending on which point is chosen for (x_1, y_1), and in general form. This way, students will see how to get from one form to the next.

How Do You See It? Exercise

Page 18, Exercise 72 Use the graphs of the equations to answer the questions below.

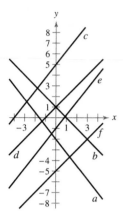

(a) Which lines have a positive slope?

(b) Which lines have a negative slope?

(c) Which lines appear parallel?

(d) Which lines appear perpendicular?

Solution

(a) Lines c, d, e, and f have positive slopes.

(b) Lines a and b have negative slopes.

(c) Lines c and e appear parallel. Lines d and f appear parallel.

(d) Lines b and f appear perpendicular. Lines b and d appear perpendicular.

Suggested Homework Assignment

Pages 16–18: 1, 11–23 odd, 27, 33, 41, 53, 61, 73, and 75.

Section P.3   Functions and Their Graphs

Section Comments

P.3   **Functions and Their Graphs**—Use function notation to represent and evaluate a function. Find the domain and range of a function. Sketch the graph of a function. Identify different types of transformations of functions. Classify functions and recognize combinations of functions.

4

Teaching Tips

Spend time reviewing the following concepts: evaluating a function and the domain and range of a function. For further review, encourage students to study the following material in *Precalculus*, 10th edition, by Larson.

- Evaluating a function: Section 1.4

- Domain and range of a function: Section 1.4

Encourage students who have access to a graphing utility or computer algebra system to use the technology to check their answers.

When evaluating a function, ask students what the function is doing with any value of x. For example, use the function:

$f(x) = 2x + 3$.

Here, the function $f(x)$ takes a value of x, multiplies it by 2 and adds 3. Have students quickly fill out $f(1)$, $f(2)$, $f(-3)$, $f(0)$, $f(a)$, $f(b)$, and f(a student's name). Follow up with asking what $f(x)$ does with stuff, $f(\text{stuff}) = 2 \times \text{stuff} + 3$. This will prove to be useful for students when evaluating functions using the difference quotient.

Be sure to spend some time evaluating functions using the difference quotient. Some suggested functions to use are: $f(x) = 2x^2 + 5x + 1$, $g(x) = \dfrac{1}{x-3}$, and $h(x) = \sqrt{x+2}$. Using $g(x)$ will test students' ability to find a least common denominator and using $h(x)$ will test students' ability to rationalize a numerator. Be sure to tell students that rationalizing the numerator will become useful in calculus.

When asking students to find the domain and range of functions, using different colored chalk or Expo markers help students visualize what the domains and ranges should be. For example, graph $f(x) = |x - 2| + 3$ and $g(x) = \sqrt{x+1} - 4$. After graphing these two functions by using the transformations, tell students that if you pick any point on either f or g and map the point back to the x- and y-axes using different colors, students will be more likely to see what the domain and ranges are. Examples of these two functions are graphed below.

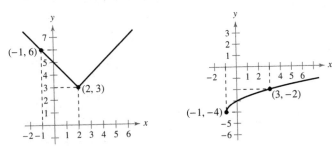

When going over the Leading Coefficient Test, start by graphing the simplest monomial functions $f(x) = x^2$ and $g(x) = x^3$. Describe the end behavior of each. Next, insert negatives and describe the end behaviors. Summarizing the results, if the degree is even with a positive leading coefficient, both ends will be rising; if a negative leading coefficient, both sides will be falling. If the degree is odd with a positive leading coefficient, the right side will be rising and the left will be falling. The opposite is true if the leading coefficient is negative. Expose students to the notation, $x \to \infty$ and $f(x) \to -\infty$ so that they will have a preview of calculus once limits are reached.

How Do You See It? Exercise

Page 30, Exercise 94

Water runs into a vase of height 30 centimeters at a constant rate. The vase is full after 5 seconds. Use this information and the shape of the vase shown to answer the questions when d is the depth of the water in centimeters and t is the time in seconds (see figure).

(a) Explain why d is a function of t.

(b) Determine the domain and range of the function.

(c) Sketch a possible graph of the function.

(d) Use the graph in part (c) to approximate $d(4)$. What does this represent?

Solution

(a) For each time t, there corresponds a depth d.

(b) Domain: $0 \le t \le 5$

      Range: $0 \le d \le 30$

(c)

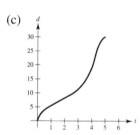

(d) $d(4) \approx 18$. At time 4 seconds, the depth is approximately 18 centimeters.

Suggested Homework Assignment

Pages 27–30: 1, 3, 7, 11, 13–21 odd, 23, 27, 35, 37, 39, 41, 45, 49, 51–61 odd, 65, 67, 69, 75, 79, 85, and 103–107 odd.

Section P.4   Review of Trigonometric Functions

Section Comments

P.4   **Review of Trigonometric Functions**—Describe angles and use degree measure. Use radian measure. Understand the definitions of the six trigonometric functions. Evaluate trigonometric functions. Solve trigonometric equations. Graph trigonometric functions.

Teaching Tips

Start by asking students to recall the unit circle, the six trigonometric functions, and the signs for each quadrant. One can review SOHCAHTOA for right triangles. For the *xy*-plane, SYRCXRTYX can also be used as shown below.

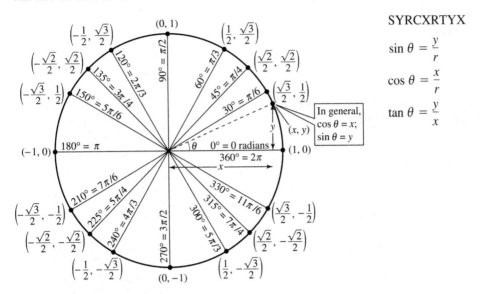

SYRCXRTYX

$$\sin \theta = \frac{y}{r}$$

$$\cos \theta = \frac{x}{r}$$

$$\tan \theta = \frac{y}{x}$$

Quickly review problems on how to convert from radians to degrees and degrees to radians. Exercises 10 and 12 are good practice for class.

Students have a difficult time solving trigonometric equations that involve multiple angles. A suggested problem to work out with students is $3 \cos x + 3 = 2 \sin^2 x$, where $0 \le x \le 2\pi$. This will test students' memory on $\sin^2 x + \cos^2 x = 1$.

Lastly, problems using the power-reducing formulas should also be presented as they will be used for trigonometric integration. For example, simplify $\sin^4 x$.

How Do You See It? Exercise

Page 40, Exercise 72 Consider an angle in standard position with $r = 12$ centimeters, as shown in the figure. Describe the changes in the values of x, y, $\sin \theta$, $\cos \theta$, and $\tan \theta$ as θ increases continually from $0°$ to $90°$.

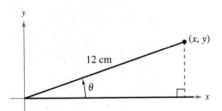

Solution

As θ increases from $0°$ to $90°$ with $r = 12$ centimeters, x decreases from 12 to 0 centimeters, y increases from 0 to 12 centimeters, $\sin \theta$ increases from 0 to 1, $\cos \theta$ decreases from 1 to 0, and $\tan \theta$ increases from 0 to (positive) infinity.

Suggested Homework Assignment

Pages 38–40: 1–15 odd, 19, 23, 29, 31–51 odd, 55–65 odd, 69, 77, and 79.

Chapter P   Project

Height of a Ferris Wheel Car

The Ferris wheel was designed by American engineer George Ferris (1859–1896). The first Ferris wheel was built for the 1893 World's Columbian Exposition in Chicago, and later used at the 1904 World's Fair in St. Louis. It had a diameter of 250 feet, and each of its 36 cars could hold 60 passengers.

Exercises

In Exercises 1–3, use the following information. A Ferris wheel with a diameter of 100 feet rotates at a constant rate of 4 revolutions per minute. Let the center of the Ferris wheel be at the origin.

1. Each of the Ferris wheel's cars travels around a circle.

    (a) Write an equation of the circle, where x and y are measured in feet.

    (b) Sketch a graph of the equation you wrote in part (a).

    (c) Use the Vertical Line Test to determine whether y is a function of x.

    (d) What does your answer to part (c) mean in the context of the problem?

2. The height h (in feet) of a Ferris wheel car located at the point (x, y) is given by

    $$h = 50 + y$$

    where y is related to the angle θ (in radians) by the equation

    $$y = 50 \sin \theta$$

    as shown in the figure.

    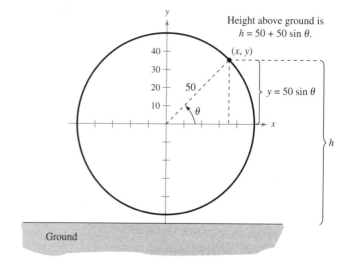

    (a) Write an equation of the height h in terms of time t (in minutes). (*Hint:* One revolution is 2π radians.)

    (b) Sketch a graph of the equation you wrote in part (a).

    (c) Use the Vertical Line Test to determine whether h is a function of t.

    (d) What does your answer to part (c) mean in the context of the problem?

3. The model in Exercise 2 yields a height of 50 feet when $t = 0$. Alter the model so that the height of the car is 0 feet when $t = 0$. Explain your reasoning.

Chapter 1 Limits and Their Properties

Chapter Comments

Section 1.1 gives a preview of calculus. On pages 47 and 48 of the textbook are examples of some of the concepts from precalculus extended to ideas that require the use of calculus. Review these ideas with your students to give them a feel for where the course is heading.

The idea of a limit is central to calculus. So, you should take the time to discuss the tangent line problem and/or the area problem in this section. Exercise 11 of Section 1.1 is yet another example of how limits will be used in calculus. A review of the formula for the distance between two points can be found in Appendix C.

The discussion of limits is difficult for most students the first time that they see it. For this reason, you should carefully go over the examples and the informal definition of a limit presented in Section 1.2. Stress to your students that a limit exists only if the answer is a real number. Otherwise, the limit fails to exist, as shown in Examples 3, 4, and 5 of this section. You might want to work Exercise 69 of Section 1.2 with your students in preparation for the definition of the number e coming up in Section 5.1. You may choose to omit the formal definition of a limit.

Carefully go over the properties of limits found in Section 1.3 to ensure that your students are comfortable with the idea of a limit and also with the notation used for limits. By the time you get to Theorem 1.6, it should be obvious to your students that all of these properties amount to direct substitution.

When direct substitution for the limit of a quotient yields the indeterminate form $\frac{0}{0}$, tell your students that they must rewrite the fraction using legitimate algebra. Then do at least one problem using dividing out techniques and another using rationalizing techniques. Exercises 58 and 60 of Section 1.3 are examples of other algebraic techniques needed for the limit problems. You need to go over the Squeeze Theorem, Theorem 1.8, with your students so that you can use it to prove $\lim_{x \to 0} \dfrac{\sin x}{x} = 1$. The proof of Theorem 1.8 and many other theorems can be found in Appendix A. Your students need to memorize both of the results in Theorem 1.9 as they will need these facts to do problems throughout the textbook. Most of your students will need help with Exercises 63–81 in this section.

Continuity, which is discussed in Section 1.4, is another idea that often puzzles students. However, if you describe a continuous function as one in which you can draw the entire graph without lifting your pencil, the idea seems to stay with them. Distinguishing between removable and nonremovable discontinuities will help students determine vertical asymptotes.

To discuss infinite limits, Section 1.5, remind your students of the graph of the function $f(x) = 1/x$ studied in Section P.3. Be sure to make your students write a vertical asymptote as an equation, not just a number. For example, for the function $y = 1/x$, the vertical asymptote is $x = 0$.

Section 1.1   A Preview of Calculus

Section Comments

1.1   **A Preview of Calculus**—Understand what calculus is and how it compares with precalculus. Understand that the tangent line problem is basic to calculus. Understand that the area problem is also basic to calculus.

9

Teaching Tips

In this first section, students see how limits arise when attempting to find a tangent to a curve. Be sure to say to students that they can think about the word *tangent* as meaning "touching" a curve at one particular point. Drawing a circle with a line that touches the circle at a specific point can illustrate tangency. Drawing a curve where a line intersects a curve twice illustrates a line that is not tangent to a curve as it crosses the curve more than once.

How Do You See It? Exercise

Page 51, Exercise 10 How would you describe the instantaneous rate of change of an automobile's position on a highway?

Solution

Answers will vary. *Sample answer:* The instantaneous rate of change of an automobile's position is the velocity of the automobile, and can be determined by the speedometer.

Suggested Homework Assignment

Page 51: 1–9 odd.

Section 1.2   Finding Limits Graphically and Numerically

Section Comments

1.2   Finding Limits Graphically and Numerically—Estimate a limit using a numerical or graphical approach. Learn different ways that a limit can fail to exist. Study and use a formal definition of limit.

Teaching Tips

In this section, we turn our focus to limits in general, and numerical and graphical ways we can find them. Ask students to consider $f(x) = \dfrac{x^2 - 4}{x - 2}$ and what is happening to $f(x)$ as x approaches 2. This will lead into the definition of a limit.

Make sure that students find limits analytically instead of using their graping utilities, as they can be misleading. For example, present to the class, $\lim\limits_{x \to 0} \sin \dfrac{\pi}{x}$. Constructing a table of values of $x = 1$, $\dfrac{1}{3}$, 0.1, $\dfrac{1}{2}$, $\dfrac{1}{4}$, and 0.01 leads to the assumption that $\lim\limits_{x \to 0} \sin \dfrac{\pi}{x} = 0$. However, this limit does not exist.

When introducing the definition of a limit, using graphs will help students understand the meaning of the definition. Suggested graphs are below:

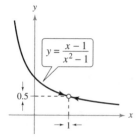
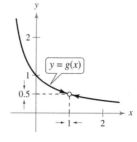

How Do You See It? Exercise

Page 62, Exercise 72 Use the graph of f to identify the values of c for which $\lim\limits_{x \to c} f(x)$ exists.

(a)

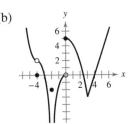

(b)

Solution

(a) $\lim\limits_{x \to c} f(x)$ exists for all $c \neq -3$.

(b) $\lim\limits_{x \to c} f(x)$ exists for all $c \neq -2, 0$.

Suggested Homework Assignment

Pages 59–60: 1, 5, 7, 15, 19, 23, 25, 27, 29, 31, and 33.

Section 1.3   Evaluating Limits Analytically

Section Comments

1.3   **Evaluating Limits Analytically**—Evaluate a limit using properties of limits. Develop and use a strategy for finding limits. Evaluate a limit using the dividing out and rationalizing techniques. Evaluate a limit using the Squeeze Theorem.

Teaching Tips

When starting this section, review how to factor using differences of two squares and two cubes, sum of two cubes, and rationalizing numerators. If you do not have time to review these concepts, encourage students to study the following material in *Precalculus*, 10th edition, by Larson.

- Factoring the difference of two squares: *Precalculus* Appendix A.3

- Factoring the difference of two cubes: *Precalculus* Appendix A.3

- Factoring the sum of two cubes: *Precalculus* Appendix A.3

- Rationalizing numerators: *Precalculus* Appendix A.2

State all limit properties as presented in this section and discuss the proper ways to write solutions when finding limits analytically. Give examples of direct substitution; some suggested examples include $\lim\limits_{x \to 2} \dfrac{x^2 - 3x + 4}{x + 2}$ and $\lim\limits_{x \to -3} 4x^3 - 5x + 1$.

When rationalizing the numerator, start with an example without limits. A suggestion is $\dfrac{\sqrt{x + 2} - \sqrt{2}}{x}$. After rationalizing the numerator, find the limit as x approaches 0.

When evaluating trigonometric limits, show students examples directly related to Theorem 1.9 in the text. Some examples are $\lim\limits_{x \to 0} \dfrac{\sin 7x}{4x}$ and $\lim\limits_{\theta \to 0} \dfrac{\cos \theta - 1}{\sin \theta}$.

How Do You See It? Exercise

Page 72, Exercise 100 Would you use the dividing out technique or the rationalizing technique to find the limit of the function? Explain your reasoning.

(a) $\lim\limits_{x \to -2} \dfrac{x^2 + x - 2}{x + 2}$

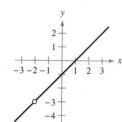

(b) $\lim\limits_{x \to 0} \dfrac{\sqrt{x + 4} - 2}{x}$

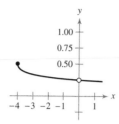

Solution

(a) Use the dividing out technique because the numerator and denominator have a common factor.

(b) Use the rationalizing technique because the numerator involves a radical expression.

Suggested Homework Assignment

Pages 71–73: 1–73 odd, 85, 95, 101, 103, and 115–119 odd.

Section 1.4   Continuity and One-Sided Limits

Section Comments

1.4 **Continuity and One-Sided Limits**—Determine continuity at a point and continuity on an open interval. Determine one-sided limits and continuity on a closed interval. Use properties of continuity. Understand and use the Intermediate Value Theorem.

Teaching Tips

Students have trouble with limits involving trigonometric functions and rationalizing denominators and numerators. Students also have trouble with limits involving rational functions. Encourage students to sharpen their algebra skills by studying the following material in the text or in *Precalculus*, 10th edition, by Larson.

- Trigonometric functions: Section P.4

- Rationalizing numerators: *Precalculus* Appendix A.2

- Simplifying rational expressions: *Precalculus* Appendix A.4

Address the following for this section:

- Describe the difference between a removable discontinuity and a nonremovable discontinuity.

- Write a function that has a removable discontinuity.

- Write a function that has a nonremovable discontinuity.

- Write a function that has a removable discontinuity and a nonremovable discontinuity.

Students will need to know these concepts when they study vertical asymptotes (Section 1.5), improper integrals (Section 8.8), and functions of several variables (Section 13.2).

12

Discuss the difference between a removable discontinuity and a nonremovable discontinuity. Use the function $f(x) = \dfrac{|x-4|}{x-4}$ to illustrate a function with a nonremovable discontinuity. Note that it is not possible to remove the discontinuity by redefining the function. When you illustrate a removable discontinuity, as in the function $f(x) = \dfrac{\sin(x+4)}{x+4}$, note that the function can be redefined to remove the discontinuity. Ask students how they would do this. (Let $f(-4) = 1$.) Finally, illustrate the example below. Show students the function and the graph, and then ask them if there are any removable or nonremovable discontinuities. Once they have properly identified $x = -4$ as removable and $x = 4$ as nonremovable, ask them to redefine f to remove the discontinuity at $x = -4$. (Let $f(-4) = 0$.)

Ask students to consider the following function with its graph below:

$$f(x) = \begin{cases} 0, & x < -4 \\ 1, & x = -4 \\ 0, & -4 < x < 4 \\ 1, & x \geq 4 \end{cases}$$

$x = 4$ is nonremovable. $x = -4$ is removable.

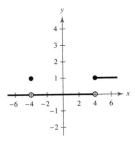

Use this example to show which are removable and nonremovable discontinuities. In addition, use a rational function with both a vertical asymptote and a hole to show the differences between removable and nonremovable discontinuities. A suggested example is $f(x) = \dfrac{8x^2 + 26x + 15}{2x^2 - x - 15}$.

How Do You See It? Exercise

Page 85, Exercise 112 Every day you dissolve 28 ounces of chlorine in a swimming pool. The graph shows the amount of chlorine $f(t)$ in the pool after t days. Estimate and interpret $\lim\limits_{t \to 4^-} f(t)$ and $\lim\limits_{t \to 4^+} f(t)$.

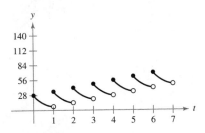

Solution

$\lim\limits_{t \to 4^-} f(t) \approx 28$

$\lim\limits_{t \to 4^+} f(t) \approx 56$

At the end of day 3, the amount of chlorine in the pool has decreased to about 28 ounces. At the beginning of day 4, more chlorine was added, and the amount is now about 56 ounces.

Suggested Homework Assignment

Pages 83–85: 1, 3, 7–19 odd, 23, 25, 27, 31, 35, 37, 47, 49, 51, 57, 61, 67, 75–81 odd, 83, 95, 97, 101, and 105–109 odd.

Section 1.5   Infinite Limits

Section Comments

1.5   **Infinite Limits**—Determine infinite limits from the left and from the right. Find and sketch the vertical asymptotes of the graph of a function.

Teaching Tips

It is vital for students to know asymptotes of a rational function for this section. Encourage students to review material on asymptotes by studying Section 2.6 in *Precalculus*, 10th edition, by Larson.

Students need to be able to decipher when vertical asymptotes versus holes will occur in a rational function. A suggested problem for students to consider is to determine if $x = 1$ is a vertical asymptote of $f(x) = \dfrac{p(x)}{x - 1}$.

In class, you can ask students who believe the graph of f has a vertical asymptote at $x = 1$ to prove it. For those who think this is not always true, ask them to provide a counterexample. A sample answer is given in the solution, and you can use the transparency to illustrate a counterexample. If desired, you could also ask students the following:

(a) At which x-values (if any) is f not continuous?

(b) Which of the discontinuities are removable?

Solution

No, it is not always true. Consider $p(x) = x^2 - 1$. The function

$$f(x) = \frac{x^2 - 1}{x - 1} = \frac{p(x)}{x - 1}$$

has a hole at $(1, 2)$, not a vertical asymptote.

How Do You See It? Exercise

Page 93, Exercise 60 For a quantity of gas at a constant temperature, the pressure P is inversely proportional to the volume V. What is the limit of P as V approaches 0 from the right? Explain what this means in the context of the problem.

Solution

$$\lim_{V \to 0^+} P = \infty$$

As the volume of the gas decreases, the pressure increases.

Suggested Homework Assignment

Pages 92–94: 1, 3, 7, 13, 17–31 odd, 37–49 odd, 53, 55, and 65–69 odd.

Chapter 1   Project

Medicine in the Bloodstream

A patient's kidneys purify 25% of the blood in her body in 4 hours.

Exercises

In Exercises 1–3, a patient takes one 16-milliliter dose of a medication.

1. Determine the amount of medication left in the patient's body after 4, 8, 12, and 16 hours.

2. Notice that after the first 4-hour period, $\frac{3}{4}$ of the 16 milliliters of medication is left in the body, after the second 4-hour period, $\frac{9}{16}$ of the 16 milliliters of medication is left in the body, and so on. Use this information to write an equation that represents the amount a of medication left in the patient's body after n 4-hour periods.

3. Can you find a value of n for which a equals 0? Explain.

In Exercises 4–9, the patient takes an additional 16-milliliter dose every 4 hours.

4. Determine the amount of medication in the patient's body immediately after taking the second dose.

5. Determine the amount of medication in the patient's body immediately after taking the third and fourth doses. What is happening to the amount of medication in the patient's body over time?

6. The medication is eliminated from the patient's body at a constant rate. Sketch a graph that shows the amount of medication in the patient's body during the first 16 hours. Let x represent the number of hours and y represent the amount of medication in the patient's body in milliliters.

7. Use the graph in Exercise 6 to find the limits.

   (a) $\lim_{x \to 4^-} f(x)$

   (b) $\lim_{x \to 4^+} f(x)$

   (c) $\lim_{x \to 12^-} f(x)$

   (d) $\lim_{x \to 12^+} f(x)$

8. Discuss the continuity of the function represented by the graph in Exercise 6. Interpret any discontinuities in the context of the problem.

9. The amount of medication in the patient's body remains constant when the amount eliminated in 4 hours is equal to the additional dose taken at the end of the 4-hour period. Write and solve an equation to find this amount.

Chapter 2 Differentiation

Chapter Comments

The material presented in Chapter 2 forms the basis for the remainder of calculus. Much of it needs to be memorized, beginning with the definition of a derivative of a function found on page 103. Students need to have a thorough understanding of the tangent line problem and they need to be able to find an equation of a tangent line. Frequently, students will use the function $f'(x)$ as the slope of the tangent line. They need to understand that $f'(x)$ is the formula for the slope and the actual value of the slope can be found by substituting into $f'(x)$ the appropriate value for x. On pages 105–106 of Section 2.1, you will find a discussion of situations where the derivative fails to exist. These examples (or similar ones) should be discussed in class.

As you teach this chapter, vary your notations for the derivative. One time write y'; another time write dy/dx or $f'(x)$. Terminology is also important. Instead of saying "find the derivative," sometimes say, "differentiate." This would be an appropriate time, also, to talk a little about Leibnitz and Newton and the discovery of calculus.

Sections 2.2, 2.3, and 2.4 present a number of rules for differentiation. Have your students memorize the Product Rule and the Quotient Rule (Theorems 2.7 and 2.8) in words rather than symbols. Students tend to be lazy when it comes to trigonometry and therefore, you need to impress upon them that the formulas for the derivatives of the six trigonometric functions need to be memorized also. You will probably not have enough time in class to prove every one of these differentiation rules, so choose several to do in class and perhaps assign a few of the other proofs as homework.

The Chain Rule, in Section 2.4, will require two days of your class time. Students need a lot of practice with this and the algebra involved in these problems. Many students can find the derivative of $f(x) = x^2\sqrt{1-x^2}$ without much trouble, but simplifying the answer is often difficult for them. Insist that they learn to factor and write the answer without negative exponents. Strive to get the answer in the form given in the back of the book. This will help them later on when the derivative is set equal to zero.

Implicit differentiation is often difficult for students. Have students think of y as a function of x and therefore y^3 is $[f(x)]^3$. This way they can relate implicit differentiation to the Chain Rule studied in the previous section.

Try to get your students to see that related rates, discussed in Section 2.6, are another use of the Chain Rule.

Section 2.1   The Derivative and the Tangent Line Problem

Section Comments

2.1   **The Derivative and the Tangent Line Problem**—Find the slope of the tangent line to a curve at a point. Use the limit definition to find the derivative of a function. Understand the relationship between differentiability and continuity.

Teaching Tips

Ask students what they think "the line tangent to a curve" means. Draw a curve with tangent lines to show a visual picture of tangent lines. For example:

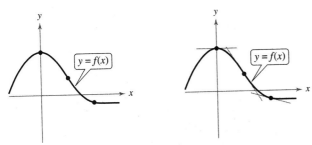

When talking about the tangent line problem, use the suggested example of finding the equation of the tangent line to the parabola $y = x^2$ at the point $(1, 1)$.

Compute an approximation of the slope m by choosing a nearby point $Q(x, x^2)$ on the parabola and computing the slope m_{PQ} of the secant line PQ.

After going over Examples 1–3, return to Example 2 where $f(x) = x^2 + 1$ and note that $f'(x) = 2x$. How can we find the equation of the line tangent to f and parallel to $4x - y = 0$? Because the slope of the line is 4,

$2x = 4$

$x = 2.$

So, at the point $(2, 5)$, the tangent line is parallel to $4x - y = 0$. The equation of the tangent line is $y - 5 = 4(x - 2)$ or $y = 4x - 3$.

Be sure to find the derivatives of various types of functions to show students the different types of techniques for finding derivatives. Some suggested problems are $f(x) = 4x^3 - 3x^2$, $g(x) = 2/(x - 1)$, and $h(x) = \sqrt{2x + 5}$.

How Do You See It? Exercise

Page 108, Exercise 64 The figure shows the graph of g'.

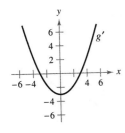

(a) $g'(0) =$

(b) $g'(3) =$

(c) What can you conclude about the graph of g knowing that $g'(1) = -\frac{8}{3}$?

(d) What can you conclude about the graph of g knowing that $g'(-4) = \frac{7}{3}$?

(e) Is $g(6) - g(4)$ positive or negative? Explain.

(f) Is it possible to find $g(2)$ from the graph? Explain.

Solution

(a) $g'(0) = -3$

(b) $g'(3) = 0$

(c) Because $g'(1) = -\frac{8}{3}$, g is decreasing (falling) at $x = 1$.

(d) Because $g'(-4) = \frac{7}{3}$, g is increasing (rising) at $x = -4$.

(e) Because $g'(4)$ and $g'(6)$ are both positive, $g(6)$ is greater than $g(4)$ and $g(6) - g(4) > 0$.

(f) No, it is not possible. All you can say is that g is decreasing (falling) at $x = 2$.

Suggested Homework Assignment

Pages 107–109: 1, 3, 7, 11, 21–27 odd, 37, 43–47 odd, 53, 57, 61, 77, 87, 93, and 95.

Section 2.2 Basic Differentiation Rules and Rates of Change

Section Comments

2.2   **Basic Differentiation Rules and Rates of Change**—Find the derivative of a function using the Constant Rule. Find the derivative of a function using the Power Rule. Find the derivative of a function using the Constant Multiple Rule. Find the derivative of a function using the Sum and Difference Rules. Find the derivatives of the sine function and of the cosine function. Use derivatives to find rates of change.

Teaching Tips

Start by showing proofs of the Constant Rule and the Power Rule. Students who are mathematics majors need to start seeing proofs early on in their college careers as they will be taking Functions of a Real Variable at some point.

Go over an example in class like $f(x) = \dfrac{5x^2 + x}{x}$. Show students that before differentiating they can rewrite the function as $f(x) = 5x + 1$. Then they can differentiate to obtain $f'(x) = 5$. Use this example to emphasize the prudence of examining the function first before differentiating. Rewriting the function in a simpler, equivalent form can expedite the differentiating process.

Give mixed examples of finding derivatives. Some suggested examples are:

$$f(x) = 3x^6 - x^{2/3} + 3\sin x \text{ and } g(x) = \frac{4}{\sqrt[3]{x}} + \frac{2}{(3x)^2} - 3\cos x + 7x + \pi^3.$$

This will test students' understanding of the various differentiation rules of this section.

How Do You See It? Exercise

Page 119, Exercise 76 Use the graph of f to answer each question. To print an enlarged copy of the graph, go to *MathGraphs.com*.

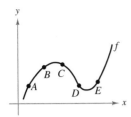

(a) Between which two consecutive points is the average rate of change of the function greatest?

(b) Is the average rate of change of the function between A and B greater than or less than the instantaneous rate of change at B?

(c) Sketch a tangent line to the graph between C and D such that the slope of the tangent line is the same as the average rate of change of the function between C and D.

Solution

(a) The slope appears to be steepest between A and B.

(b) The average rate of change between A and B is **greater** than the instantaneous rate of change at B.

(c)

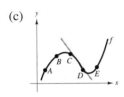

Suggested Homework Assignment

Pages 118–120: 1, 3, 5, 7–29 odd, 35, 39–53 odd, 55, 59, 65, 75, 85–89 odd, 91, 95, and 97.

Section 2.3 Product and Quotient Rules and Higher-Order Derivatives

Section Comments

2.3   **Product and Quotient Rules and Higher-Order Derivatives**—Find the derivative of a function using the Product Rule. Find the derivative of a function using the Quotient Rule. Find the derivative of a trigonometric function. Find a higher-order derivative of a function.

Teaching Tips

Some students have difficulty simplifying polynomial and rational expressions. Students should review these concepts by studying Appendices A.2–A.4 and A.7 in *Precalculus*, 10th edition, by Larson.

When teaching the Product and Quotient Rules, give proofs of each rule so that students can see where the rules come from. This will provide mathematics majors a tool for writing proofs, as each proof requires subtracting and adding the same quantity to achieve the desired results. For the Project Rule, emphasize that there are many ways to write the solution. Remind students that there must be one derivative in each term of the solution. Also, the Product Rule can be extended to more that just the product of two functions. Simplification is up to the discretion of the instructor. Examples such as $f(x) = (2x^2 - 3x)(5x^3 + 6)$ can be done with or without the Product Rule. Show the class both ways.

After the Quotient Rule has been proved to the class, give students the memorization tool of LO d HI – HI d LO. This will give students a way to memorize what goes in the numerator of the Quotient Rule.

Some examples to use are $f(x) = \dfrac{2x - 1}{x^2 + 7x}$ and $g(x) = \dfrac{4 - (1/x)}{3 - x^2}$. Save $f(x)$ for the next section as this will be a good example for the Chain Rule. $g(x)$ is a good example for first finding the least common denominator.

How Do You See It? Exercise

Page 132, Exercise 120 The figure shows the graphs of the position, velocity, and acceleration functions of a particle.

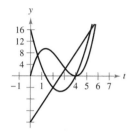

(a) Copy the graphs of the functions shown. Identify each graph. Explain your reasoning. To print an enlarged copy of the graph, go to *MathGraphs.com*.

(b) On your sketch, identify when the particle speeds up and when it slows down. Explain your reasoning.

Solution

(a)

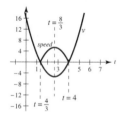

s position function

v velocity function

a acceleration function

(b) The speed of the particle is the absolute value of its velocity. So, the particle's speed is slowing down on the intervals $(0, 4/3)$, and $(8/3, 4)$ and it speeds up on the intervals $(4/3, 8/3)$ and $(4, 6)$.

Suggested Homework Assignment

Pages 129–132: 1, 3, 9, 13, 19, 23, 29–55 odd, 59, 61, 63, 75, 77, 91–107 odd, 111, 113, 117, and 131–135 odd.

Section 2.4 The Chain Rule

Section Comments

2.4 **The Chain Rule**—Find the derivative of a composite function using the Chain Rule. Find the derivative of a function using the General Power Rule. Simplify the derivative of a function using algebra. Find the derivative of a trigonometric function using the Chain Rule.

Teaching Tips

Begin this section by asking students to consider finding the derivative of $F(x) = \sqrt{x^2 + 1}$. F is a composite function. Letting $y = f(u) = \sqrt{u}$ and $u = g(x) = x^2 + 1$, then $y = F(x) = f(g(x))$ or $F = f \circ g$. When stating the Chain Rule, be sure to state it using function notation and using Leibniz notation as students will see both forms when studying other courses with other texts. Following the definition, be sure to prove the Chain Rule as done on page 134.

Be sure to give examples that involve all rules discussed so far. Some examples include:

$$f(x) = (\sin(6x))^4, \ g(x) = \left(\frac{3 + \sin(2x)}{\sqrt[3]{x + 3}}\right)^2, \text{ and } h(x) = \left(\sqrt{x - \frac{2}{x}}\right) \cdot [8x + \cos(x^2 + 1)]^3.$$

You can use Exercise 98 on page 141 to review the following concepts:

- Product Rule

- Chain Rule

- Quotient Rule

- General Power Rule

Students need to understand these rules because they are the foundation of the study of differentiation.

Use the solution to show students how to solve each problem. As you apply each rule, give the definition of the rule verbally. Note that part (b) is not possible because we are not given $g'(3)$.

Solution

(a) $f(x) = g(x)h(x)$

$f'(x) = g(x)h'(x) + g'(x)h(x)$

$f'(5) = (-3)(-2) + (6)(3) = 24$

(b) $f(x) = g(h(x))$

$f'(x) = g'(h(x))h'(x)$

$f'(5) = g'(3)(-2) = -2g'(3)$

Not possible. You need $g'(3)$ to find $f'(5)$.

(c) $f(x) = \dfrac{g(x)}{h(x)}$

$f'(x) = \dfrac{h(x)g'(x) - g(x)h'(x)}{[h(x)]^2}$

$f'(x) = \dfrac{(3)(6) - (-3)(-2)}{(3)^2} = \dfrac{12}{9} = \dfrac{4}{3}$

(d) $f(x) = [g(x)]^3$

$f'(x) = 3[g(x)]^2 g'(x)$

$f'(5) = 3(-3)^2(6) = 162$

How Do You See It? Exercise

Page 142, Exercise 106 The cost C (in dollars) of producing x units of a product is $C = 60x + 1350$. For one week, management determined that the number of units produced x at the end of t hours can be modeled by $x = -1.6t^3 + 19t^2 - 0.5t - 1$. The graph shows the cost C in terms of the time t.

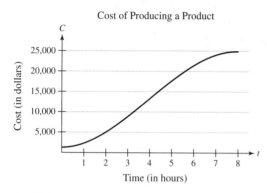

Cost of Producing a Product

(a) Using the graph, which is greater, the rate of change of the cost after 1 hour or the rate of change of the cost after 4 hours?

(b) Explain why the cost function is not increasing at a constant rate during the eight-hour shift.

Solution

(a) According to the graph, $C'(4) > C'(1)$.

(b) Answers will vary.

Suggested Homework Assignment

Pages 140–143: 1–53 odd, 63, 67, 75, 81, 83, 91, 97, 121, and 123.

Section 2.5 Implicit Differentiation

Section Comments

2.5   **Implicit Differentiation**—Distinguish between functions written in implicit form and explicit form. Use implicit differentiation to find the derivative of a function.

Teaching Tips

Material learned in this section will be vital for students to have for related rates. Be sure to ask students to find $\dfrac{dy}{dx}$ when $x = c$.

You can use the exercise below to review the following concepts:

- Finding derivatives when the variables agree and when they disagree

- Using implicit differentiation to find the derivative of a function

Determine if the statement is true. If it is false, explain why and correct it. For each statement, assume y is a function of x.

(a) $\dfrac{d}{dx}\cos(x^2) = -2x\sin(x^2)$

(b) $\dfrac{d}{dy}\cos(y^2) = 2y\sin(y^2)$

(c) $\dfrac{d}{dx}\cos(y^2) = -2y\sin(y^2)$

Implicit differentiation is often difficult for students, so as you review this concept remind students to think of y as a function of x. Part (a) is true, and part (b) can be corrected as shown below. Part (c) requires implicit differentiation. Note that the result can also be written as $-2y\sin(y^2)\,\dfrac{dy}{dx}$.

Solution

(a) True

(b) False. $\dfrac{d}{dy}\cos(y^2) = -2y\sin(y^2)$.

(c) False. $\dfrac{d}{dx}\cos(y^2) = -2yy'\sin(y^2)$.

A good way to teach students how to understand the differentiation of a mix of variables in part (c) is to let $g = y$. Then $g' = y'$. So,

$$\frac{d}{dx}\cos(y^2) = \frac{d}{dx}\cos(g^2)$$

$$= -\sin(g^2)\cdot 2gg'$$

$$= -\sin(y^2)\cdot 2yy'$$

How Do You See It? Exercise

Page 151, Exercise 70 Use the graph to answer the questions.

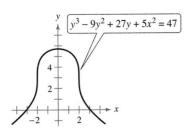

(a) Which is greater, the slope of the tangent line at $x = -3$ or the slope of the tangent line at $x = -1$?

(b) Estimate the point(s) where the graph has a vertical tangent line.

(c) Estimate the point(s) where the graph has a horizontal tangent line.

Solution

(a) The slope is greater at $x = -3$.

(b) The graph has vertical tangent lines at about $(-2, 3)$ and $(2, 3)$.

(c) The graph has a horizontal tangent line at about $(0, 6)$.

23

Section 2.6 Related Rates

Section Comments

2.6   Related Rates—Find a related rate. Use related rates to solve real-life problems.

Teaching Tips

Begin this lesson with a quick review of implicit differentiation with an implicit function in terms of x and y differentiated with respect to time. Follow this with an example similar to Example 1 on page 152, outlining the step-by-step procedure at the top of page 153 along with the guidelines at the bottom of page 153. Be sure to tell students, that for every related rate problem, to write down the given information, the equation needed, and the unknown quantity. A suggested problem to work out with the students is as follows:

A ladder 10 feet long rests against a vertical wall. If the bottom of the ladder slides away from the wall at a rate of 1 foot per second, how fast is the top of the ladder sliding down the wall when the bottom of the ladder is 6 feet from the wall?

Be sure to go over a related rate problem similar to Example 5 on page 155 so that students are exposed to working with related rate problems involving trigonometric functions.

How Do You See It? Exercise

Page 159, Exercise 34 Using the graph of f, (a) determine whether dy/dt is positive or negative given that dx/dt is negative, and (b) determine whether dx/dt is positive or negative given that dy/dt is positive. Explain.

(i) 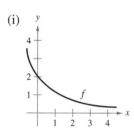   (ii)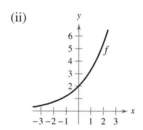

Solution

(i) (a) $\dfrac{dx}{dt}$ negative $\implies$ $\dfrac{dy}{dt}$ positive

     (b) $\dfrac{dy}{dt}$ positive $\implies$ $\dfrac{dx}{dt}$ negative

(ii) (a) $\dfrac{dx}{dt}$ negative $\implies$ $\dfrac{dy}{dt}$ negative

     (b) $\dfrac{dy}{dt}$ positive $\implies$ $\dfrac{dx}{dt}$ positive

Chapter 2 Project

Timing a Handoff

You are a competitive bicyclist. During a race, you bike at a constant velocity of k meters per second. A chase car waits for you at the ten-mile mark of a course. When you cross the ten-mile mark, the car immediately accelerates to catch you. The position function of the chase car is given by the equation $s(t) = \frac{15}{4}t^2 - \frac{5}{12}t^3$, for $0 \le t \le 6$, where t is the time in seconds and s is the distance traveled in meters. When the car catches you, you and the car are traveling at the same velocity, and the driver hands you a cup of water while you continue to bike at k meters per second.

Exercises

1. Write an equation that represents your position s (in meters) at time t (in seconds).

2. Use your answer to Exercise 1 and the given information to write an equation that represents the velocity k at which the chase car catches you in terms of t.

3. Find the velocity function of the car.

4. Use your answers to Exercises 2 and 3 to find how many seconds it takes the chase car to catch you.

5. What is your velocity when the car catches you?

6. Use a graphing utility to graph the chase car's position function and your position function in the same viewing window.

7. Find the point of intersection of the two graphs in Exercise 6. What does this point represent in the context of the problem?

8. Describe the graphs in Exercise 6 at the point of intersection. Why is this important for a successful handoff?

9. Suppose you bike at a constant velocity of 9 meters per second and the chase car's position function is unchanged.

    (a) Use a graphing utility to graph the chase car's position function and your position function in the same viewing window.

    (b) In this scenario, how many times will the chase car be in the same position as you after the 10-mile mark?

    (c) In this scenario, would the driver of the car be able to successfully handoff a cup of water to you? Explain.

10. Suppose you bike at a constant velocity of 8 meters per second and the chase car's position function is unchanged.

    (a) Use a graphing utility to graph the chase car's position function and your position function in the same viewing window.

    (b) In this scenario, how many times will the chase car be in the same position as you after the ten-mile mark?

    (c) In this scenario, why might it be difficult for the driver of the chase car to successfully handoff a cup of water to you? Explain.

Chapter 3   Applications of Differentiation

Chapter Comments

Chapter 3 considers some of the applications of a derivative. The first five sections in this chapter lead up to analyzing the graph of a function in Section 3.6. Before beginning this material, you may want to quickly review with your students the ideas of intercepts, vertical asymptotes, and symmetry with respect to the *x*-axis, the *y*-axis, and the origin. These algebraic tools covered in Chapter P are needed, along with those from calculus, in order to analyze the graph of a function.

Don't get bogged down in Section 3.1. The students need to know the terminology, so stress the definitions of critical numbers and extrema. Section 3.2 covers Rolle's Theorem and the Mean Value Theorem. Rolle's Theorem is used to prove the Mean Value Theorem.

Sections 3.3 and 3.4 cover the bulk of the material necessary to analyze the graphs of functions. Go over these sections carefully.

In Section 3.5, limits at infinity and horizontal asymptotes are discussed. Be sure to require that your students write horizontal asymptotes as lines: for example, $y = 3$.

Section 3.6 contains a summary of all of the ideas involved in analyzing the graph of a function. Note that slant asymptotes are covered in the comment after Example 2. After this material is covered, each day until you finish the chapter, assign one or two carefully chosen graphing problems. Have your students make a list of all of the tools useful in sketching a graph: intercepts, asymptotes, symmetry, critical numbers, increasing and decreasing intervals, extrema, concavity, and inflection points. Only after this list is completed should the function be sketched.

If your students know the material in Sections 3.1 through 3.6 well, then the optimization problems in Section 3.7 should go fairly well for them. Stress the difference between a primary and a secondary equation. Also, stress the need to have the function in one independent variable before attempting to maximize or minimize it.

Newton's Method, covered in Section 3.8, is a tool that students of future math and science courses will be expected to know. A calculator is needed.

You should be able to cover differentials in Section 3.9 quickly. Students need to understand that a differential is a reasonable approximation for the actual difference in function values.

Section 3.1   Extrema on an Interval

Section Comments

3.1   **Extrema on an Interval**—Understand the definition of extrema of a function on an interval. Understand the definition of relative extrema of a function on an open interval. Find extrema on a closed interval.

Teaching Tips

Start out this lesson by drawing a graph with various relative and absolute maximums and minimums so students can visualize what each look like. An example of a graph of a function is shown below:

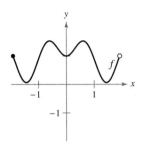

Tell students that they can view maximums as being the peaks of mountains and minimums as the valleys.

When all of the maximums and minimums have been identified, change one of the maximums or minimums to a sharp point and discuss if the function is continuous and differentiable at that sharp point. This will also lead to discussion about whether the point is a maximum or minimum.

In addition, change one of the endpoints of the graph so that there is a hole. Discuss the continuity, differentiability, and if there exists a maximum or minimum at that hole.

How Do You See It? Exercise

Page 172, Exercise 56 Determine whether each labeled point is an absolute maximum or minimum, a relative maximum or minimum, or none of these.

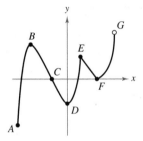

Solution

A: absolute minimum

B: relative maximum

C: neither

D: relative minimum

E: relative maximum

F: relative minimum

G: neither

Suggested Homework Assignment

Pages 171–173: 1–5 odd, 9, 17–39 odd, 59, 65, and 67.

Section 3.2 Rolle's Theorem and the Mean Value Theorem

Section Comments

3.2   **Rolle's Theorem and the Mean Value Theorem**—Understand and use Rolle's
        Theorem. Understand and use the Mean Value Theorem.

Teaching Tips

Rolle's Theorem and the Mean Value Theorem should be stated and if time allows, proved in
class. Use a partially graphed function to start the lesson in order for students to see how the
two theorems play a vital role in calculus. A suggested graph is:

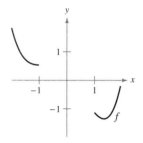

Questions for the class can include:

(a) Explain why f must have at least one real zero in $[-1, 1.5]$.

(b) Explain why f must also have at least one real zero in the interval $[-1, 1.5]$.

(c) Make a possible sketch of the function with one real zero of f on the interval $[-1, 1.5]$.

It should be stressed that the figure shows two parts of the graph of a continuous differentiable
function f on $[-1, 1.5]$.

How Do You See It? Exercise

Page 180, Exercise 64 The figure shows two parts of the graph of a continuous differentiable
function f on $[-10, 4]$. The derivative f' is also continuous. To print an enlarged copy of the
graph, go to *MathGraphs.com*.

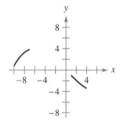

(a) Explain why f must have at least one zero in $[-10, 4]$.

(b) Explain why f' must also have at least one zero in the interval $[-10, 4]$. What are these
    zeros called?

(c) Make a possible sketch of the function, where f' has one zero on the interval $[-10, 4]$.

Solution

(a) f is continuous on $[-10, 4]$ and changes sign, $(f(-8) > 0, f(3) < 0)$. By the Intermediate Value Theorem, there exists at least one value of x in $[-10, 4]$ satisfying $f(x) = 0$.

(b) There exist real numbers a and b such that $-10 < a < b < 4$ and $f(a) = f(b) = 2$. Therefore, by Rolle's Theorem there exists at least one number c in $(-10, 4)$ such that $f'(c) = 0$. This is called a critical number.

(c)

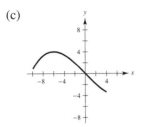

Suggested Homework Assignment

Pages 178–180: 1, 3, 9, 13, 17, 21, 29, 33, 41, 43, 47, 61, 73, and 75.

Section 3.3 Increasing and Decreasing Functions and the First Derivative Test

Section Comments

3.3   Increasing and Decreasing Functions and the First Derivative Test—Determine intervals on which a function is increasing or decreasing. Apply the First Derivative Test to find relative extrema of a function.

Teaching Tips

Use the exercise below to review the following concepts:

- Increasing and decreasing functions

- Theorem 3.5

- Guidelines for finding intervals on which a function is increasing or decreasing

- Theorem 3.6

- Applying the First Derivative Test

A differentiable function f has one critical number at $x = 5$. Identify the relative extrema of f at the critical number if $f'(4) = -2.5$ and $f'(6) = 3$.

These concepts, along with those taught in Section 3.4, cover most of the material necessary to analyze graphs of functions. Before going over this exercise, you may want to restate Theorems 3.5 and 3.6.

You can use this exercise to show students how to apply the guidelines for finding intervals on which a function is increasing or decreasing (see page 182). As you go over the following, make a table similar to the one given in Example 1 on page 182.

1. Note that the only critical number of the differentiable function f is $x = 5$. So, the test intervals are $-\infty < x < 5$ and $5 < x < \infty$.

2. We are given the value of the derivative of f at two test values, $x = 4$ and $x = 6$. In the interval $-\infty < x < 5$, we know $f'(4) = -2.5$. In the interval $5 < x < \infty$, we know $f'(6) = 3$.

3. By Theorem 3.5, f is decreasing on $(-\infty, 5)$ and increasing on $(5, \infty)$.

We can now apply the First Derivative Test to conclude that f has a relative minimum at the point where $x = 5$.

Solution

Critical number: $x = 5$

$f'(4) = -2.5 \implies f$ is decreasing at $x = 4$.

$f'(6) = 3 \quad \implies f$ is increasing at $x = 6$.

$(5, f(5))$ is a relative minimum.

How Do You See It? Exercise

Page 188, Exercise 70 Use the graph of f' to (a) identify the critical numbers of f, (b) identify the open interval(s) on which f is increasing or decreasing, and (c) determine whether f has a relative maximum, a relative minimum, or neither at each critical number.

(i)

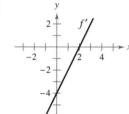

(ii)

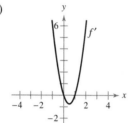

(iii)

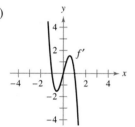

(iv)

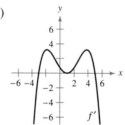

Solution

(i) (a) Critical number: $x = 2$ (Because $f'(2) = 0$)

   (b) f increasing on $(2, \infty)$ (Because $f' > 0$ on $(2, \infty)$)

   f decreasing on $(-\infty, 2)$ (Because $f' < 0$ on $(-\infty, 2)$)

   (c) f has a relative minimum at $x = 2$.

(ii) (a) Critical numbers: $x = 0, 1$ (Because $f'(1) = 0$)

   (b) f increasing on $(-\infty, 0)$ and $(1, \infty)$ (Because $f' > 0$ on these intervals)

   f decreasing on $(0, 1)$ (Because $f' < 0$ on $(0, 1)$)

   (c) f has a relative maximum at $x = 0$ and a relative minimum at $x = 1$.

(iii) (a) Critical numbers: $x = -1, 0, 1$ (Because $f'(-1) = f'(0) = f'(1) = 0$)

   (b) f increasing on $(-\infty, -1)$ and $(0, 1)$ (Because $f' > 0$ on these intervals)

      f decreasing on $(-1, 0)$ and $(1, \infty)$ (Because $f' < 0$ on these intervals)

   (c) f has a relative maximum at $x = -1$ and $x = 1$. f has a relative minimum at $x = 0$.

(iv) (a) Critical numbers: $x = -3, 1, 5$ (Because $f'(-3) = f'(1) = f'(5) = 0$)

   (b) f increasing on $(-3, 1)$ and $(1, 5)$ (Because $f' > 0$ on these intervals)
      In fact, f is increasing on $(-3, 5)$.

      f decreasing on $(-\infty, -3)$ and $(5, \infty)$ (Because $f' < 0$ on these intervals)

   (c) f has a relative minimum at $x = -3$ and a relative maximum at $x = 5$.
      $x = 1$ is not a relative extremum.

Suggested Homework Assignment

Pages 187–190: 1, 7, 9, 11–47 odd, 57–69 odd, 73, 83, 91, 93, and 95.

Section 3.4 Concavity and the Second Derivative Test

Section Comments

3.4   **Concavity and the Second Derivative Test**—Determine intervals on which a function
is concave upward or concave downward. Find any points of inflection of the graph of
a function. Apply the Second Derivative Test to find relative extrema of a function.

Teaching Tips

Start this lesson by asking students why is it true that if f is concave upward, all tangent lines to f
lie below the curve? Ask the same question if f is concave downward.

You can use the teaching tip that concave upward will hold water and concave downward will
spill water as shown in the picture below.

(a)

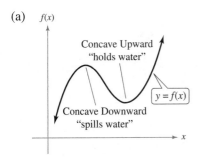

(b)

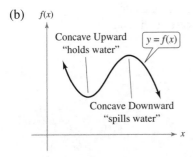

When dealing with a concave upward part of a function, all slopes to tangent lines must be positive and increasing in slope. The opposite is true if the part of the function is concave downward as shown below.

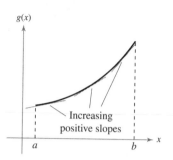 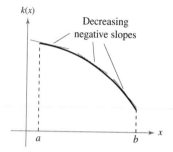

Present a problem similar to Example 2 on page 193 where no points of inflection exist. Also, present a problem similar to Example 4 on page 195 where the Second Derivative Test fails.

How Do You See It? Exercise

Page 197, Exercise 58 Water is running into the vase shown in the figure at a constant rate.

(a) Graph the depth d of water in the vase as a function of time.

(b) Does the function have any extrema? Explain.

(c) Interpret the inflection points of the graph of d.

Solution

(a)

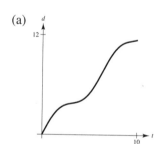

(b) Because the depth d is always increasing, there are no relative extrema. $f'(x) > 0$

(c) The rate of change of d is decreasing until you reach the widest point of the jug, then the rate increases until you reach the narrowest part of the jug's neck, then the rate decreases until you reach the top of the jug.

Suggested Homework Assignments

Pages 196–198: 1, 7, 13, 17, 31, 33–43 odd, 49–55 odd, 75, and 77.

Section 3.5 Limits at Infinity

Section Comments

3.5   **Limits at Infinity**—Determine (finite) limits at infinity. Determine the horizontal asymptotes, if any, of the graph of a function. Determine infinite limits at infinity.

Teaching Tips

To give students an initial understanding of limits at infinity, construct a table of values for a function that has a horizontal asymptote. A suggested function is $f(x) = \dfrac{2x^3}{4x^3 - 4x^2}$. By constructing a table of values and graphing f, students will see that as x approaches either positive or negative infinity, f approaches $\frac{1}{2}$. The point should be made that this rational function does have a horizontal asymptote at $x = \frac{1}{2}$ and the degree of both the numerator and denominator are the same. So, taking the ratio of the leading coefficients of the numerator and denominator gives

$$x = \frac{2}{4} = \frac{1}{2}.$$

Use the exercise below to review the following concepts:

- Given the graph of a function f, sketch f'.

- Use a graph to estimate limits at infinity.

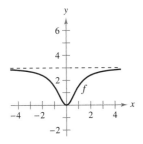

Use the graph of f to:

(a) Sketch f'.

(b) Use the graph to estimate $\lim\limits_{x \to \infty} f(x)$ and $\lim\limits_{x \to \infty} f'(x)$.

(c) Explain the solutions to parts (a) and (b).

To sketch f', use the graph of f. Note from the graph that f is decreasing on $-4 < x < 0$, so $f' < 0$ on $-4 < x < 0$. Because f is increasing on $0 < x < 4$, $f' > 0$ on $0 < x < 4$. The graph of f' should also reflect the rate of change of f. The graph of f changes rapidly as it approaches 0 from the left, slows at 0, and then the rate increases and then slows again as f nears the line $y = 3$. As x increases, f approaches the line $y = 3$ and the rate of change of f approaches 0. Make sure students realize that $y = 3$ is a horizontal asymptote of the graph of f.

Solution

(a)

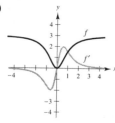

(b) $\lim\limits_{x\to\infty} f(x) = 3$

$\lim\limits_{x\to\infty} f'(x) = 0$

(c) Because $\lim\limits_{x\to\infty} f(x) = 3$, the graph approaches that of a horizontal line, $\lim\limits_{x\to\infty} f'(x) = 0$.

How Do You See It? Exercise

Page 207, Exercise 56 The graph shows the temperature T, in degrees Fahrenheit, of molten glass t seconds after it is removed from a kiln.

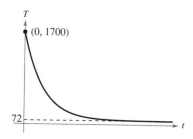

(a) Find $\lim\limits_{t\to 0^+} T$. What does this limit represent?

(b) Find $\lim\limits_{t\to\infty} T$. What does this limit represent?

Solution

(a) $\lim\limits_{t\to 0^+} T = 1700°$

This is the temperature of the kiln.

(b) $\lim\limits_{t\to\infty} T = 72°$

This is the temperature of the room.

Suggested Homework Assignment

Pages 206–207: 1–13 odd, 15–35 odd, 39, 43, and 53.

Section 3.6 A Summary of Curve Sketching

Section Comments

3.6   A Summary of Curve Sketching—Analyze and sketch the graph of a function.

Teaching Tips

A question that should be posed to the class before starting this lesson is: Why can't we just create a table of values for each function, plot the points in the *xy*-plane, and connect the points to sketch a graph of $f(x)$? The answers students give will vary, but two good answers will include that it is possible to miss small extrema when plotting points and plotting points will not give a good graphical presentation of asymptotes.

When going through the process of curve sketching, it is helpful for students to make small pictures when determining if the first and second derivatives are positive and negative. This will give them a better understanding of where the function is increasing, decreasing, concave upward, and concave downward; where the points of inflections are; and where the maximums and minimums exist. A suggested picture is shown for $f(x) = 2x^3 - 3x^2 - 12x + 1$.

Interval	$(-\infty, -1)$	$(-1, 1/2)$	$(1/2, 2)$	$(2, \infty)$
Sign of f'	+	−	−	+
Sign of f''	−	−	+	+
f Increasing or Decreasing	Increasing	Decreasing	Decreasing	Increasing
Concavity of f	Downward	Downward	Upward	Upward
Shape of Graph	⌒	⌒	⌣	⌣

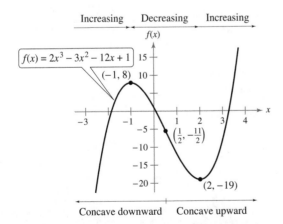

Use Exercise 78 on page 217 to review the following concepts:

- Critical numbers

- Horizontal tangent

- Relative extrema

- Points of inflection

- Concavity

You can use this exercise to review the important definitions and theorems taught in Sections 3.1–3.5. Note in part (c) that x_1 is a critical number. Some students miss this and answer "none" for part (d).

Solution

(a) $f'(x) = 0$ at x_0, x_2, and x_4 (horizontal tangent).

(b) $f''(x) = 0$ at x_2 and x_3 (point of inflection).

(c) $f'(x)$ does not exist at x_1 (sharp corner).

(d) f has a relative maximum at x_1.

(e) f has a point of inflection at x_2 and x_3 (change in concavity).

How Do You See It? Exercise

Page 217, Exercise 64 The graph of f is shown in the figure.

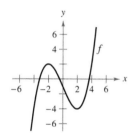

(a) For which values of x is $f'(x)$ zero? Positive? Negative? What do these values mean?

(b) For which values of x is $f''(x)$ zero? Positive? Negative? What do these values mean?

(c) On what open interval is f' an increasing function?

(d) For which value of x is $f'(x)$ minimum? For this value of x, how does the rate of change of f compare with the rates of change of f for other values of x? Explain.

Solution

(a) $f'(x) = 0$ for $x = -2$ (relative maximum) and $x = 2$ (relative minimum).

 f' is negative for $-2 < x < 2$ (decreasing).

 f' is positive for $x > 2$ and $x < -2$ (increasing).

(b) $f''(x) = 0$ at $x = 0$ (point of inflection).

 f'' is positive for $x > 0$ (concave upward).

 f'' is negative for $x < 0$ (concave downward).

(c) f' is increasing on $(0, \infty)$. $(f'' > 0)$

(d) $f'(x)$ is minimum at $x = 0$. The rate of change of f at $x = 0$ is less than the rate of change of f for all other values of x.

Suggested Homework Assignment

Pages 215–218: 1–7 odd, 13, 19, 25, 33, 37, 51, 55, 59, 61, 83, and 85.

Section 3.7 Optimization Problems

Section Comments

3.7   **Optimization Problems**—Solve applied minimum and maximum problems.

Teaching Tips

When introducing students to optimization problems for the first time, outline the key points to successfully solving these types of problems.

1. Use the method outlined in the text on page 220.

2. Use the various tests already seen during the semester and the closed interval method for finding extrema.

3. Check results on a graphing utility and ask yourself, does the answer make sense in the physical world?

4. Use implicit differentiation.

Begin with a simple problem involving finding the maximum area: If a farmer has 2400 feet of fence and wants to fence off his rectangular field that borders a river, what are the dimensions of the field that has the largest area?

Use the exercise below to review the following concepts:

- Analyzing an optimization problem

- Reviewing the guidelines for solving applied minimum and maximum problems

The perimeter of a rectangle is 20 feet. Of all possible dimensions, the maximum area is 25 square feet when its length and width are both 5 feet. Are there dimensions that yield a minimum area?

You can use this exercise to show students that not all optimization problems have a maximum and a minimum. Draw several rectangles that have a perimeter of 20 feet, such as $l = 6$ and $w = 4$. Also draw a rectangle where the length and width are both 5 feet. For rectangles with a perimeter of 20 feet, this rectangle yields the maximum area. Ask students, "What dimensions will yield a minimum area?" Use the solution below to show students that no such dimensions exist. Use the solution as an opportunity to review the guidelines for solving applied minimum and maximum problems. Note in Step 4 of the guidelines that no values exist for which the stated problem will make sense.

Solution

No, there is no minimum area. If the sides are x and y, then $2x + 2y = 20 \implies y = 10 - x$. The area is $A(x) = x(10 - x) = 10x - x^2$. This can be made arbitrarily small by selecting $x \approx 0$.

How Do You See It? Exercise

Page 227, Exercise 48 The graph shows the profit P (in thousands of dollars) of a company in terms of its advertising cost x (in thousands of dollars).

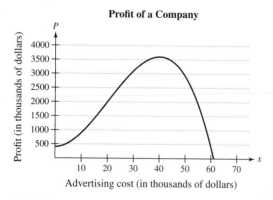

Profit of a Company

(a) Estimate the interval on which the profit is increasing.

(b) Estimate the interval on which the profit is decreasing.

(c) Estimate the amount of money the company should spend on advertising in order to yield a maximum profit.

(d) The *point of diminishing returns* is the point at which the rate of growth of the profit function begins to decline. Estimate the point of diminishing returns.

Solution

(a) The profit is increasing on $(0, 40)$.

(b) The profit is decreasing on $(40, 60)$.

(c) In order to yield a maximum profit, the company should spend about $40 thousand.

(d) The point of diminishing returns is the point where the concavity changes, which in this case is $x = 20$ thousand dollars.

Suggested Homework Assignment

Pages 224–226: 1, 7, 11–19 odd, 29, 33, 39, and 41.

Section 3.8 Newton's Method

Section Comments

3.8   **Newton's Method**—Approximate a zero of a function using Newton's Method.

Teaching Tips

Ask students when using Newton's method to find a root, how do you know what to pick for x_1?

Use the following sample problem:

Use Newton's method to find x_4, the fourth approximation of the positive root of $x^3 - 3x - 5 = 0$. Students can choose their own x_1.

How Do You See It? Exercise

Page 234, Exercise 32 For what value(s) will Newton's Method fail to converge for the function shown in the graph? Explain your reasoning.

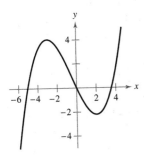

Solution

At $x = -3$ and $x = 2$, the tangent lines to the curve are horizontal. Hence, Newton's Method will not converge for these initial approximations.

Suggested Homework Assignment

Pages 233–234: 1, 3, 9, 19, 23, 31, 37, and 39.

Section 3.9 Differentials

Section Comments

3.9 **Differentials**—Understand the concept of a tangent line approximation. Compare the value of the differential, dy, with the actual change in y, Δy. Estimate a propagated error using a differential. Find the differential of a function using differentiation formulas.

Teaching Tips

As a first example after the definition of differentials has been discussed, find the equation of the line that best approximates the graph of $y = \cos x + x$ at the point $(0, 1)$. Discuss the meaning of approximating along the tangent line and its connection to a linear approximation.

Use the exercise below to review the following concept:

- Understanding the concept of a tangent line approximation

  Would you use $y = x$ to approximate $f(x) = \sin x$ near $x = 0$? Why or why not?

Use the solution below. (You may want to model your presentation of this solution after the one used in Example 1 on page 235.) Also, sketch the graph of f and $y = x$ near $x = 0$.

Solution

Yes. $y = x$ is the tangent line approximation to $f(x) = \sin x$ at $(0, 0)$.

$f'(x) = \cos x$

$f'(0) = 1$

Tangent line: $y - 0 = 1(x - 0)$

$$y = x$$

How Do You See It? Exercise

Page 241, Exercise 38 The graph shows the profit P (in dollars) from selling x units of an item. Use the graph to determine which is greater, the change in profit when the production level changes from 400 to 401 units or the change in profit when the production level changes from 900 to 901 units. Explain your reasoning.

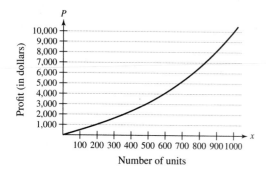

Solution

Because the slope of the tangent line is greater at $x = 900$ than at $x = 400$, the change in profit is greater at $x = 900$ units.

Suggested Homework Assignment

Pages 240–241: 1, 3, 7, 17, 19–27 odd, 33, 35, 43, 47, 49, and 51.

Chapter 3 Project

Maximum and Minimum Temperature

In a 24-hour period, a human's body temperature will vary about 3 degrees. When at rest (usually at night), the body conserves heat and the body temperature drops. During activity (usually in the daytime), the body produces heat and the body temperature rises. This situation can be modeled by the periodic function $y = 1.8 \sin^3\left(\frac{\pi}{12}x - \frac{\pi}{2}\right) + 98.6$, where y represents the body's temperature (in degrees Fahrenheit) and x represents time, with $x = 0$, corresponding to 12 A.M.

Exercises

1. Find the derivative of $y = 1.8 \sin^3\left(\frac{\pi}{12}x - \frac{\pi}{2}\right) + 98.6$.

2. Find the critical numbers of $y = 1.8 \sin^3\left(\frac{\pi}{12}x - \frac{\pi}{2}\right) + 98.6$ on the interval $[0, 24]$.

3. During the course of a 24-hour period, at what time(s) is a human's body temperature greatest? During the course of a 24-hour period, at what time(s) is a human's body temperature least? What theorem did you use?

4. Use a graphing utility to graph $y = 1.8 \sin^3\left(\frac{\pi}{12}x - \frac{\pi}{2}\right) + 98.6$. What occurs when $x = 6$ and $x = 18$? What does this mean in the context of the problem?

5. A person who works third shift rests during the day and is active at night. Alter the function to model the body temperature of a third-shift worker.

6. Find the critical numbers of the function you wrote in Exercise 5 on the interval $[0, 24]$.

7. During the course of a 24-hour period, at what time(s) is the body temperature of a third-shift worker greatest? During the course of a 24-hour period, at what time(s) is the body temperature of a third-shift worker least?

8. Use a graphing utility to graph the equation you wrote in Exercise 5. What occurs when $x = 6$ and $x = 18$? Compare this to your answer to Exercise 4. What is different about these points for the third-shift worker?

9. Suppose the body temperature of a second-shift worker can be modeled by shifting $y = 1.8 \sin^3\left(\frac{\pi}{12}x - \frac{\pi}{2}\right) + 98.6$ six units to the right. Write an equation to model the body temperature of a second-shift worker.

10. Find the critical numbers of the function you wrote in Exercise 9 on the interval $[0, 24]$.

11. During the course of a 24-hour period, at what time(s) is the body temperature of a second-shift worker greatest? During the course of a 24-hour period, at what time(s) is the body temperature of a second-shift worker least?

Chapter 4 Integration

Chapter Comments

The first section of this chapter stresses correct terminology and notation. Recognizing the different ways to express the same algebraic expression is very important. Algebra will get a workout. As you introduce antiderivatives, insist that your students write the proper differential when they write an integral problem. Deduct points on homework and quizzes for incorrect notation.

Some of your students may not have seen sigma notation previously, so introduce it as though it is a new topic. The idea of the limit of a sum as n approaches infinity should go quickly if the students learned the rules for limits at infinity from Section 3.5. If you are pressed for time, you may want to briefly go over area using a limit definition (as done in Section 4.2). For example, you could do one problem to show the idea and the technique, and then move on to Section 4.3.

The amount of time spent on Riemann sums will depend on your schedule and your class. The definite integral is defined in Section 4.3, as is area. Be sure that your students set up the limits for area properly. Do not accept integrals for area with the upper and lower limits interchanged.

Students should know the Fundamental Theorem of Calculus by name and have it memorized. The Mean Value Theorem for Integrals and the average value of a function are covered in Section 4.4. The Second Fundamental Theorem of Calculus is used in the definition of the natural logarithmic function, so be sure to go over it.

It is important for your students to be comfortable with all of the integration techniques covered in Section 4.5. Allow two days to cover these ideas and go over each carefully. Be sure to do some change of variable problems, a technique that many students are reluctant to use.

Section 4.1 Antiderivatives and Indefinite Integration

Section Comments

4.1   **Antiderivatives and Indefinite Integration**—Write the general solution of a differential equation and use indefinite integral notation for antiderivatives. Use basic integration rules to find antiderivatives. Find a particular solution of a differential equation.

Teaching Tips

For this section, students often have trouble rewriting the integrand in a form that fits the basic integration rules. You may want to cover Example 7 given on page 252 (before the section exercises) in class. Students have trouble with integrands like the one in Exercise 25, so do an example such as the following.

$$\int \frac{x^3 + 1}{\sqrt{x}}\, dx = \int \left(x^{5/2} + x^{-1/2}\right) dx = \frac{x^{7/2}}{7/2} + \frac{x^{1/2}}{1/2} + C = \frac{2}{7}x^{7/2} + 2x^{1/2} + C$$

You can use the "How Do You See It?" exercise to review the following concepts:

- Using the graph of f' to make conclusions about f

- First Derivative Test

- Increasing and decreasing functions

- Concavity

- Relative extrema

- Discovering relationships between a function and its antiderivative

How Do You See It? Exercise

Page 256, Exercise 52 Use the graph of f' shown in the figure to answer the following.

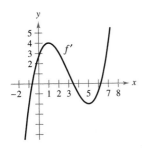

(a) Approximate the slope of f at $x = 4$. Explain.

(b) Is $f(5) - f(1) > 0$? Explain.

(c) Approximate the value of x where f is maximum. Explain.

(d) Approximate any open intervals on which the graph of f is concave upward and any open intervals on which it is concave downward. Approximate the x-coordinates of any points of inflection.

Solution

$f(0) = -4$. Graph of f' is given.

(a) $f'(4) \approx -1.0$

(b) No, $f(5) < f(4)$ because f is decreasing on $[4, 5]$.

(c) f is a maximum at $x = 3.5$ because $f'(3.5) \approx 0$ and the First Derivative Test.

(d) f is concave upward when f' is increasing on $(-\infty, 1)$ and $(5, \infty)$. f is concave downward on $(1, 5)$. Points of inflection at $x = 1, 5$.

Suggested Homework Assignment

Pages 255–257: 1, 3, 11–35 odd, 49, 51, 57–61 odd, 65, 71, and 73–77 odd.

Section 4.2 Area

Section Comments

4.2 **Area**—Use sigma notation to write and evaluate a sum. Understand the concept of area. Approximate the area of a plane region. Find the area of a plane region using limits.

Teaching Tips

Ask students to consider the function $f(x) = x^2$ and ask them why is it true that for any closed interval $[a, b]$ with $a > 0$, every left endpoint sum is less than the area under f from a to b and every right endpoint sum is greater than that area?

After addressing the question above, ask students to look at the equation, $d = rt$. If you want to find the distance of something traveling at a constant rate, this will represent an area under the curve as shown on the left. However, if you want to find the area under a curve such as the one on the right, you then must use rectangles to approximate the area.

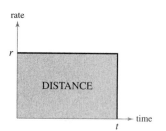

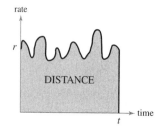

rate constant: distance = shaded area

rate varies: distance = shaded area (still)

You can lead students to become familiar with the fact that choosing left endpoints for a decreasing function leads to an overestimate and choosing right endpoints leads to an underestimate.

Students should have visual pictures either drawn on the board or on a handout for the different situations of midpoints and left and right endpoints, under- and overestimates, and increasing and decreasing functions.

How Do You See It? Exercise

Page 269, Exercise 72 The function shown in the graph below is increasing on the interval $[1, 4]$. The interval will be divided into 12 subintervals.

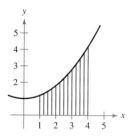

(a) What are the left endpoints of the first and last subintervals?

(b) What are the right endpoints of the first two subintervals?

(c) When using the right endpoints, do the rectangles lie above or below the graph of the function?

(d) What can you conclude about the heights of the rectangles when the function is constant on the given interval?

Solution

(a) Left endpoint of first subinterval is 1.

   Left endpoint of last subinterval is $4 - \frac{1}{4} = \frac{15}{4}$.

(b) Right endpoint of first subinterval is $1 + \frac{1}{4} = \frac{5}{4}$.

   Right endpoint of second subinterval is $1 + \frac{1}{2} = \frac{3}{2}$.

(c) The rectangles lie above the graph.

(d) The heights would be equal to that constant.

Suggested Homework Assignment

Pages 267–269: 1, 3, 5, 11–15 odd, 21, 23, 31, 33, 39, 53, 67, and 73.

Section 4.3 Riemann Sums and Definite Integrals

Section Comments

4.3   Riemann Sums and Definite Integrals—Understand the definition of a Riemann sum. Evaluate a definite integral using limits and geometric formulas. Evaluate a definite integral using properties of definite integrals.

Teaching Tips

Students often have difficulty seeing the relationship between area and the definite integral. Present students with a graph of a function and ask students to find various integrals and areas. An example is shown below, where $A_1 = \frac{11}{6}$, $A_2 = -\frac{9}{2}$, and $A_3 = \frac{11}{6}$.

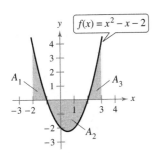

(a) $\displaystyle\int_{-2}^{-1} f(x)\,dx =$

(b) $\displaystyle\int_{-2}^{2} f(x)\,dx =$

(c) $\displaystyle\int_{-1}^{3} f(x)\,dx =$

You may also want to have students work on the following group activity:

Consider the constant function $f(t) = 4$.

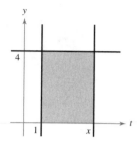

(a) Using geometry, evaluate $\int_1^2 f(t)\, dt$.

(b) Similarly, evaluate $\int_1^3 f(t)\, dt$ and $\int_1^4 f(t)\, dt$.

(c) Using your answers to parts (a) and (b) as a guide, compute $\int_1^x f(t)\, dt$ for any $x \geq 1$.

(d) Define the *area function* $A(x) = \int_1^x f(t)\, dt$, $1 \leq x \leq 4$. What is $A(2)$? $A(2.5)$? $A(1)$? Write a general formula for $A(x)$.

How Do You See It? Exercise

Page 279, Exercise 50 Use the figure to fill in the blank with the symbol $<$, $>$, or $=$. Explain your reasoning.

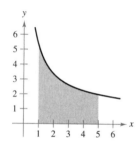

(a) The interval $[1, 5]$ is partitioned into n subintervals of equal width Δx, and x_i is the left endpoint of the ith subinterval.

$$\sum_{i=1}^n f(x_i)\, \Delta x \quad\rule{1cm}{0.4cm}\quad \int_1^5 f(x)\, dx$$

(b) The interval $[1, 5]$ is partitioned into n subintervals of equal width Δx, and x_i is the right endpoint of the ith subinterval.

$$\sum_{i=1}^n f(x_i)\, \Delta x \quad\rule{1cm}{0.4cm}\quad \int_1^5 f(x)\, dx$$

Solution

(a) The left endpoint approximation will be greater than the actual area so,

$$\sum_{i=1}^n f(x_i)\, \Delta x > \int_1^5 f(x)\, dx.$$

(b) The right endpoint approximation will be less than the actual area so,

$$\sum_{i=1}^5 f(x_i)\, \Delta x < \int_1^5 f(x)\, dx.$$

Section 4.4 The Fundamental Theorem of Calculus

Section Comments

4.4   **The Fundamental Theorem of Calculus**—Evaluate a definite integral using the
Fundamental Theorem of Calculus. Understand and use the Mean Value Theorem for
Integrals. Find the average value of a function over a closed interval. Understand and use the
Second Fundamental Theorem of Calculus. Understand and use the Net Change Theorem.

Teaching Tips

Be sure to address the differences between $\int f(x)\,dx$ and $\int_a^b f(x)\,dx$. Depending on the amount of
time in class, you may wish to give a proof of the Fundamental Theorem of Calculus. This will be
especially useful for the mathematics majors to see. Ask students why the theorem is *fundamental*.
Connections should be made between differentiation and integration.

A group activity to motivate the first part of the Fundamental Theorem of Calculus is to consider
$g(x) = \int_0^x f(t)\,dt$ and to evaluate $g(x)$ for $x = 1, 2, 2.5,$ and 3, and to determine where $g(x)$ has
maximums and minimums (see graph below).

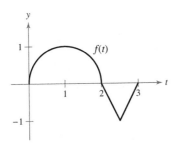

How Do You See It? Exercise

Page 293, Exercise 62 The graph of f is shown in the figure. The shaded region A has an
area of 1.5, and $\int_0^6 f(x)\,dx.$ Use this information to fill in the blanks.

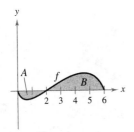

(a) $\displaystyle\int_0^2 f(x)\,dx = $ ▨

(b) $\displaystyle\int_2^6 f(x)\,dx = $ ▨

(c) $\displaystyle\int_0^6 |f(x)|\,dx = $ ▨

(d) $\displaystyle\int_0^2 -2f(x)\,dx = $ ▨

(e) $\displaystyle\int_0^6 [2 + f(x)]\,dx = $ ▨

(f) The average value of f over the interval $[0, 6]$ is ▨ .

Solution

(a) Because $y < 0$ on $[0, 2]$, $\displaystyle\int_0^2 f(x)\,dx = -(\text{area of region } A) = -1.5$.

(b) $\displaystyle\int_2^6 f(x)\,dx = (\text{area of region } B) = \int_0^6 f(x)\,dx = -\int_0^2 f(x)\,dx = 3.5 - (-1.5) = 5.0$

(c) $\displaystyle\int_0^6 |f(x)|\,dx = -\int_0^2 f(x)\,dx + \int_2^6 f(x)\,dx = 1.5 + 5.0 = 6.5$

(d) $\displaystyle\int_0^2 -2f(x)\,dx = -2\int_0^2 f(x)\,dx = -2(-1.5) = 3.0$

(e) $\displaystyle\int_0^6 [2 + f(x)]\,dx = \int_0^6 2\,dx + \int_0^6 f(x)\,dx = 12 + 3.5 = 15.5$

(f) Average value $= \dfrac{1}{6}\displaystyle\int_0^6 f(x)\,dx = \dfrac{1}{6}(3.5) = 0.5833$

Suggested Homework Assignment

Pages 292–295: 1, 3, 9–35 odd, 43, 47, 55, 59, 75–85 odd, 95, and 109.

Section 4.5 Integration by Substitution

Section Comments

4.5 **Integration by Substitution**—Use pattern recognition to find an indefinite integral. Use a change of variables to find an indefinite integral. Use the General Power Rule for Integration to find an indefinite integral. Use a change of variables to evaluate a definite integral. Evaluate a definite integral involving an even or odd function.

Teaching Tips

We suggest using the problem below to review the following concepts:

- Using pattern recognition to find an indefinite integral

- Theorem 4.13

- Using the Constant Multiple Rule to rewrite an integrand

- Using the General Power Rule for Integration to find an indefinite integral

Find each indefinite integral in two ways. Explain any difference in the forms of the answers.

(a) $\displaystyle\int (2x - 1)^2\,dx$

(b) $\displaystyle\int \sin x \cos x\,dx$

(c) $\displaystyle\int \tan x \sec^2 x\,dx$

It is important for students to be comfortable with these integration techniques. In part (a), note the use of the Constant Multiple Rule to rewrite the integrand to obtain the pattern $f(g(x))g'(x)$ where $g(x) = 2x - 1$. Then use the Power Rule for Integration and Theorem 4.13 as shown. The second way is to expand the binomial and then integrate the polynomial function (see Section 4.1).

In parts (b) and (c), you can demonstrate substitution and the General Power Rule. (See Example 7.) You may need to review the differentiation rules for sine, cosine, tangent, and secant to help students see the $u^n\,du$ pattern. Also, you will need to use the identities $\sin^2 x + \cos^2 x = 1$ and $\tan^2 x + 1 = \sec^2 x$ to explain the difference in the forms of the answers.

Solution

(a) $\displaystyle\int (2x - 1)^2\,dx = \frac{1}{2}\int (2x - 1)^2 2\,dx = \frac{1}{6}(2x - 1)^3 + C_1 = \frac{4}{3}x^3 - 2x^2 + x - \frac{1}{6} + C_1$

$\displaystyle\int (2x - 1)^2\,dx = \int (4x^2 - 4x + 1)\,dx = \frac{4}{3}x^3 - 2x^2 + x + C_2$

They differ by a constant: $C_2 = C_1 - \dfrac{1}{6}$.

(b) $\displaystyle\int \sin x \cos x\,dx = \int (\sin x)^1(\cos x\,dx) = \frac{\sin^2 x}{2} + C_1$

$\displaystyle\int \sin x \cos x\,dx = -\int (\cos x)^1(-\sin x\,dx) = -\frac{\cos^2 x}{2} + C_2$

$-\dfrac{\cos^2 x}{2} + C_2 = -\dfrac{(1 - \sin^2 x)}{2} + C_2 = \dfrac{\sin^2 x}{2} - \dfrac{1}{2} + C_2$

They differ by a constant: $C_2 = C_1 + \dfrac{1}{2}$.

(c) $\displaystyle\int \tan x \sec^2 x\,dx = \frac{\tan^2 x}{2} + C_1$

$\displaystyle\int \tan x \sec^2 x\,dx = \int \sec x(\sec x \tan x)\,dx = \frac{\sec^2 x}{2} + C_2$

$\dfrac{\tan^2 x}{2} + C_1 = \dfrac{\sec^2 x - 1}{2} + C_1 = \dfrac{\sec^2 x}{2} - \dfrac{1}{2} + C_1$

They differ by a constant: $C_2 = C_1 - \dfrac{1}{2}$.

How Do You See It? Exercise

Page 307, Exercise 84 The graph shows the flow rate of water at a pumping station for one day.

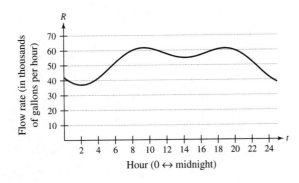

(a) Approximate the maximum flow rate at the pumping station. At what time does this occur?

(b) Explain how you can find the amount of water used during the day.

(c) Approximate the two-hour period when the least amount of water is used. Explain your reasoning.

Solution

(a) The maximum flow is approximately $R \approx 62$ thousand gallons at 9:00 A.M. ($t \approx 9$).

(b) The volume of water used during the day is the area under the curve for $0 \le t \le 24$. That is,

$$V = \int_0^{24} R(t)\, dt.$$

(c) The least amount of water is used approximately from 1 A.M. to 3 A.M. ($1 \le t \le 3$).

Suggested Homework Assignment

Pages 305–308: 1–29 odd, 39–77 odd, 81, and 93–97 odd.

Chapter 4 Project

Ordering Siding

You need to determine the amount of wood siding needed for a barn.

Exercises

1. The curve that forms the roof of the barn is a semicircle.

   (a) Write an equation of the semicircle. Let the center of the circle be at the origin.

   (b) Approximate the area of the semicircle using the formula for the area of a circle.

   (c) Set up a definite integral that yields the area of the semicircle.

   (d) Use a graphing utility to evaluate the integral you wrote in part (c). Compare this to your answer from part (b).

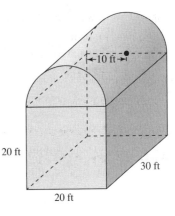

2. Based on your findings in Exercise 1, determine the total area to be sided. (The roof of the barn does not need siding.)

3. One-foot wide siding is laid vertically as shown in the figure.

   (a) Graph the equation of the semicircle from Exercise 1 and draw the rectangles representing the upper sum for this situation. Explain why it is important to use an upper sum in this context.

   (b) Find the lengths of the wood pieces that must be ordered to completely side the barn. Because the wood must be cut to the nearest foot, round all lengths up to the nearest foot. Organize the lengths in a table as shown.

Dimensions of Board	Number of Pieces
1 ft by _____	

   (c) According to your answer from part (b), how many square feet of wood should be ordered?

   (d) Use your answers from Exercise 2 and part (c) to determine how much wood is wasted.

   (e) What happens to the amount of wasted wood if the width of the siding increases? Decreases? Explain.

4. Repeat Exercise 3. One-foot wide siding is laid horizontally as shown in the figure.

5. What recommendations would you make in order to side the barn most efficiently? Explain.

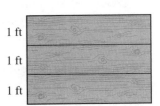

Chapter 5 Logarithmic, Exponential, and Other Transcendental Functions

Chapter Comments

Although students should be familiar and comfortable with both the logarithmic and exponential functions, they frequently are not. So, present these functions as though they are new ideas. Have your students commit to memory the graphs and properties of these functions. You should review the Second Fundamental Theorem of Calculus, covered in Section 4.4, before introducing the definition of the natural logarithmic function. Be sure to go over logarithmic differentiation as done in Example 6 of Section 5.1.

Integrals that yield a natural logarithmic function are hard for students to see at first. You must tell students that whenever the problem is $\int f(x)/g(x)\, dx$ there are two things to consider before anything else:

1. If the degree of $f(x) \geq$ the degree of $g(x)$, then perform algebraic long division to rewrite the integrand.

2. Investigate for the possibility of u'/u.

Notice that with Theorem 5.5, you can now integrate all six of the trigonometric functions. These integration rules, found on page 329, are important; have your students memorize them. The problems in the exercises for Section 5.2 bring out a number of important concepts for integration. Be sure to allow enough time to go over these thoroughly.

Students should be familiar with inverse functions from their algebra courses, so perhaps Section 5.3 could be covered quickly. However, a thorough discussion of exponential functions in Section 5.4 is necessary. This section covers the definition, properties, derivative, and integral of the natural exponential function. Although not especially difficult, it is a lot of new material at one time, so go over it carefully. Be sure to do a problem involving previously covered ideas, such as extrema or area.

Section 5.5 could be covered lightly if time is a problem. However, students will need to be able to differentiate a^u in Chapter 9, so be sure to cover Theorem 5.13.

When you cover indeterminate forms and L'Hôpital's Rule in Section 5.6, be sure to do Example 5 on page 366 because that limit turns out to be the number e. Some books use this limit as a definition of e and your students need to recognize it, as it comes up in the problems later on.

Inverse trigonometric functions, covered in Sections 5.7 and 5.8, will not appeal to your students. They tend to get lazy when the trigonometry gets this involved. Section 5.7 contains a table of Basic Differentiation Rules for Elementary Functions that all students of calculus should know.

In Section 5.8, there are some examples that demonstrate important tools that will be needed for future work with integration. The rewriting of the integrand as the sum of two quotients is shown in Example 3. Completing the square for a quadratic expression is demonstrated in Examples 4 and 5. These examples should be done in class. Again, remind students of the need to divide if the degree of the polynomial in the numerator is greater than or equal to the degree of the polynomial in the denominator. The problems for Section 5.8 contain a significant amount of information, reviewing all that you know about integration so far. You should plan to spend quite a bit of time covering them. Exercise 41 would be a good example to do with your students in class after they have attempted Exercises 1–39 on their own.

Section 5.9 discusses hyperbolic functions and could be covered lightly if you are pressed for time. Do not omit completely, however, because students will see these functions again.

52

Section 5.1 The Natural Logarithmic Function: Differentiation

Section Comments

5.1   **The Natural Logarithmic Function: Differentiation**—Develop and use properties of the natural logarithmic function. Understand the definition of the number e. Find derivatives of functions involving the natural logarithmic function.

Teaching Tips

You may want to do an example in class on finding an equation of a tangent line to the graph of a logarithmic function. Also, you can assign the Interactive Example for Example 3. This investigation allows students to use the derivative of a natural logarithmic function and review finding a tangent line to the graph of a function, open intervals on which a function is increasing or decreasing, and relative extrema of a function.

Remind students that the logarithmic properties given in Theorem 5.2 can be used to simplify differentiation involving products, quotients, and powers (see Example 4).

We suggest using the example below to review the following concepts:

- Using properties of the natural logarithmic function

- Finding a derivative of a function involving the natural logarithmic function

- Using a derivative to find rates of change

Given $f(x) = \ln x^a$, where a is a real number such that $a > 0$, determine the rates of change of $f(x)$ when (a) $x = 10$ and (b) $x = 100$.

Note in the solution the use of Property 3 from Theorem 5.2 (see page 316) to rewrite $\ln x^a$ as $a \ln x$. Students tend to forget to use Theorem 5.2 to simplify functions before differentiating. After simplifying, you can show students how to apply Theorem 5.3 (see page 318). Now use the derivative to find rates of change (see Section 2.2). After studying antiderivatives in Chapter 4, students may need a refresher on this and other previously covered ideas, such as extrema (see Example 8, page 320).

Solution

$f(x) = \ln x^a = a \ln x$

$f'(x) = \dfrac{a}{x}$

(a) When $x = 10$, $f'(x) = \dfrac{a}{10}$.

(b) When $x = 100$, $f'(x) = \dfrac{a}{100}$.

How Do You See It? Exercise

Page 322, Exercise 98   The graph shows the temperature T (in degrees Celsius) of an object h hours after it is removed from a furnace.

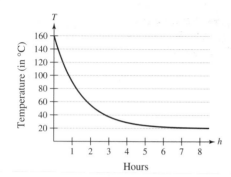

(a) Find $\lim\limits_{h\to\infty} T$. What does this limit represent?

(b) When is the temperature changing most rapidly?

Solution

(a) $\lim\limits_{h\to\infty} T = 20$

The temperature of the object seems to approach 20°C, which is the temperature of the surrounding medium.

(b) The temperature changes most rapidly when it is first removed from the furnace. The slope is steepest at $h = 0$.

Suggested Homework Assignment

Pages 321–322: 1, 3, 15, 17, 23, 25, 33, 39, 43–65 odd, 71, 75–83 odd, 95, 99, and 101.

Section 5.2 The Natural Logarithmic Function: Integration

Section Comments

5.2   **The Natural Logarithmic Function: Integration**—Use the Log Rule for Integration to integrate a rational function. Integrate trigonometric functions.

Teaching Tips

Be sure that your students memorize the integration rules given on page 329 and go over Example 10.

When introducing the concept of finding derivatives using $\ln[f(x)]$, use:

$$\frac{d}{dx}[\ln(f(x))] = \frac{1}{f(x)} \cdot f'(x).$$

Use the problem below to review the following concepts:

- Definition of the natural logarithmic function

- Log Rule for Integration

- Definition of e

Find the value of x such that $\displaystyle\int_{1}^{x} \frac{1}{t}\, dt$ equals (a) ln 5 and (b) 1.

Assume $x > 0$ and note that the integral is the definition of the natural logarithmic function (see page 314). Apply the Log Rule for Integration to obtain $\ln x$. Then solve the logarithmic equations in parts (a) and (b) as shown. Note the use of the definition of e (see page 317) in part (b).

Solution

$$\int_1^x \frac{1}{t}\, dt = \left[\ln|t| \right]_1^x = \ln x \quad (\text{Assume } x > 0.)$$

(a) $\ln x = \ln 5 \implies x = 5$

(b) $\ln x = 1 \implies x = e$

How Do You See It? Exercise

Page 332, Exercise 96 Use the graph of f' shown in the figure to answer the following.

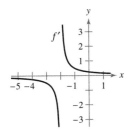

(a) Approximate the slope of f at $x = -1$. Explain.

(b) Approximate any open intervals in which the graph of f is increasing and any open intervals in which it is decreasing. Explain.

Solution

(a) At $x = -1$, $f'(-1) \approx \frac{1}{2}$. The slope of f at $x = -1$ is approximately $\frac{1}{2}$.

(b) Because the slope is positive for $x > -2$, f is increasing on $(-2, \infty)$. Similarly, f is decreasing on $(-\infty, -2)$.

Suggested Homework Assignment

Pages 330–332: 1–27 odd, 33–41 odd, 47, 51–57 odd, 61–75 odd, 97, and 99.

Section 5.3 Inverse Functions

Section Comments

5.3 **Inverse Functions**—Verify that one function is the inverse function of another function. Determine whether a function has an inverse function. Find the derivative of an inverse function.

Teaching Tips

Be sure to go over Theorem 5.9 and evaluating the derivative of an inverse function as done in Example 5. The direction line is written to have students use the function f and the given real number a to find

$$(f^{-1})'(a).$$

Use the sample problem below to review the following concepts:

- Definition of inverse function

- Theorems 5.6 and 5.9

- Graphs of inverse functions have reciprocal slopes.

The point $(1, 3)$ lies on the graph of $f(x)$, and the slope of the tangent line through this point is $m = 2$. Assume f^{-1} exists. What is the slope of the tangent line to the graph of f^{-1} at the point $(3, 1)$?

Students should be familiar with inverse functions from their algebra courses. Because of this, you may be covering this material quickly. If so, you can use this exercise to quickly review the definition of inverse function (see page 333). Because the point $(1, 3)$ lies on the graph of f and by Theorem 5.6, you know that the point $(3, 1)$ lies on the graph of f^{-1}. It follows from Theorem 5.9 (see pages 337 and 338) that the slope of f^{-1} at $(3, 1)$ is $\frac{1}{2}$.

Solution

Because the slope of f at $(1, 3)$ is $m = 2$, the slope of f^{-1} at $(3, 1)$ is $\frac{1}{2}$.

How Do You See It? Exercise

Page 341, Exercise 88 Use the information in the graph of f below.

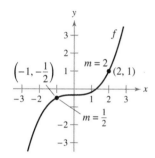

(a) What is the slope of the tangent line to the graph of f^{-1} at the point $\left(-\frac{1}{2}, -1\right)$? Explain.

(b) What is the slope of the tangent line to the graph of f^{-1} at the point $(1, 2)$? Explain.

Solution

(a) Because the slope of the tangent line to f at $\left(-1, -\frac{1}{2}\right)$ is $\frac{1}{2}$, the slope of the tangent line to f^{-1} at $\left(-\frac{1}{2}, 1\right)$ is

$$m = \frac{1}{(1/2)} = 2.$$

(b) Because the slope of the tangent line to f at $(2, 1)$ is 2, the slope of the tangent line to f^{-1} at $(1, 2)$ is

$$m = \frac{1}{2}.$$

Suggested Homework Assignment

Pages 339–341: 1–17 odd, 27, 33, 41, 51, 63–71 odd, 75, 81, and 89.

Section 5.4 Exponential Functions: Differentiation and Integration

Section Comments

5.4   **Exponential Functions: Differentiation and Integration**—Develop properties of the natural exponential function. Differentiate natural exponential functions. Integrate natural exponential functions.

Teaching Tips

Be thorough in your coverage of the definition, properties, derivative, and integral of the natural exponential function. This is a lot of new material at one time.

When introducing the concept of finding derivatives using $e^{f(x)}$, use:

$$\frac{d}{dx}[e^{f(x)}] = e^{f(x)} \cdot f'(x).$$

Using function notation will help students realize how to differentiate using the natural base e.

When integrating $\int e^{kx} \, dx$, tell students that this form will always be

$$\int e^{kx} \, dx = \frac{1}{k}e^{kx} + C.$$

Use the sample problem below to review the following concept:

- The inverse relationship between the natural logarithmic function and the natural exponential function

Describe the relationship between the graphs of $f(x) = \ln x$ and $g(x) = e^x$.

Review the definition of the natural exponential function on page 342. Use a graph like Figure 5.18 and include the line $y = x$.

Solution

The graphs of $f(x) = \ln x$ and $g(x) = e^x$ are mirror images across the line $y = x$.

How Do You See It? Exercise

Page 349, Exercise 82 The figure shows the graphs of f and g, where a is a positive real number. Identify the open interval(s) on which the graphs of f and g are (a) increasing or decreasing and (b) concave upward or concave downward.

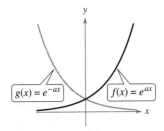

Solution

(a) f is increasing on $(-\infty, \infty)$. g is decreasing on $(-\infty, \infty)$.

(b) f and g are both concave upward on $(-\infty, \infty)$.

Pages 348–351: 1, 7, 17, 33–53 odd, 61, 65, 91–117 odd, 125, 131, and 133.

Section 5.5 Bases Other than *e* and Applications

Section Comments

5.5   **Bases Other than *e* and Applications**—Define exponential functions that have bases other than *e*. Differentiate and integrate exponential functions that have bases other than *e*. Use exponential functions to model compound interest and exponential growth.

Teaching Tips

Be sure students are able to differentiate a^u as they will need this skill in Chapter 9.

Use the sample problem below to review the following concepts:

- Defining an exponential function that has a base other than *e*

- Defining a logarithmic function to base *a*

- Finding an exponential function to model a table of values

- Finding a logarithmic function to model a table of values

The table of values below was obtained by evaluating a function. Determine which of the statements may be true and which must be false, and explain why.

x	1	2	8
y	0	1	3

(a) *y* is an exponential function of *x*.

(b) *y* is a logarithmic function of *x*.

(c) *x* is an exponential function of *y*.

(d) *y* is a linear function of *x*.

Review the definitions of exponential and logarithmic functions to base *a* on pages 352 and 353. Use the transparency to show the graph of the table of values.

Solution

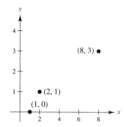

x	1	2	8
y	0	1	3

(a) y is an exponential function of x: False

(b) y is a logarithmic function of x: True; $y = \log_2 x$

(c) x is an exponential function of y: True; $2^y = x$

(d) y is a linear function of x: False

How Do You See It? Exercise

Page 360, Exercise 100 The graph shows the proportion P of correct responses after n trials in a group project in learning theory.

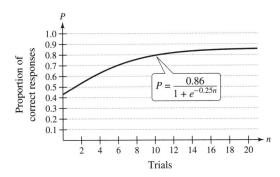

(a) What is the limiting proportion of correct responses as n approaches infinity?

(b) What happens to the rate of change of the proportion in the long run?

Solution

$$P = \frac{0.86}{1 + e^{-0.25m}}$$

(a) $\displaystyle\lim_{n\to\infty} \frac{0.86}{1 + e^{-0.25n}} = \frac{0.86}{1} = 0.86$, or 86%

(b) In the long run, $\dfrac{dP}{dn} \to 0$. The graph gets flatter.

Suggested Homework Assignment

Pages 358–360: 1, 3, 39–59 odd, 63, 69–81 odd, and 97.

Section 5.6 Indeterminate Forms and L'Hôpital's Rule

Section Comments

5.6   Indeterminate Forms and L'Hôpital's Rule—Recognize limits that produce indeterminate forms. Apply L'Hôpital's Rule to evaluate a limit.

Teaching Tips

Begin this lesson by asking students to find $\displaystyle\lim_{x\to\infty} \frac{e^x}{x^2}$. Here, students will find that each limit in the numerator and denominator tend to infinity. Ask students why you don't take the derivative of $\dfrac{e^x}{x^2}$.

Lead students to the answer that you are using L'Hôpital's Rule to evaluate $\displaystyle\lim_{x\to\infty} \frac{f(x)}{g(x)} = \lim_{x\to\infty} \frac{f'(x)}{g'(x)}$.

A follow-up question could be: $\displaystyle\lim_{x\to\infty} \frac{4x + \tan x}{\sin x}$.

Stress to students that $\dfrac{\infty}{\infty}, \dfrac{0}{0}, 0 \cdot \infty, 1^\infty, 0^0$, and $\infty - \infty$ are each called indeterminate forms. Ask students to come up with various examples that lead to an indeterminate form.

Other good examples to work out with the class are: $\displaystyle\lim_{x \to 0^+} \sin x \ln x$, $\displaystyle\lim_{x \to \infty} (1 + x)^{1/x}$, and $\displaystyle\lim_{x \to 0^+} (1 + x)^{1/x}$.

Use Exercise 65 to review the following concept:

  • L'Hôptial's Rule

Go over Theorem 5.17 and the solution below.

Solution

(a) Yes: $\dfrac{0}{0}$

(b) No: $\dfrac{0}{-1}$

(c) Yes: $\dfrac{\infty}{\infty}$

(d) Yes: $\dfrac{0}{0}$

(e) No: $\dfrac{-1}{0}$

(f) Yes: $\dfrac{0}{0}$

How Do You See It? Exercise

Page 370, Exercise 66 Use the graph of f to find the limit.

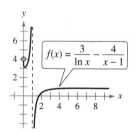

$f(x) = \dfrac{3}{\ln x} - \dfrac{4}{x - 1}$

(a) $\displaystyle\lim_{x \to 1^-} f(x)$ (b) $\displaystyle\lim_{x \to 1^+} f(x)$ (c) $\displaystyle\lim_{x \to 1} f(x)$

Solution

(a) From the graph, $\displaystyle\lim_{x \to 1^-} f(x) = \infty$.

(b) From the graph, $\displaystyle\lim_{x \to 1^+} f(x) = -\infty$.

(c) From the graph, $\displaystyle\lim_{x \to 1} f(x)$ does not exist.

Suggested Homework Assignment

Pages 369–371: 1, 5, 7–61 odd, and 95–99 odd.

Section 5.7 Inverse Trigonometric Functions: Differentiation

Section Comments

5.7   **Inverse Trigonometric Functions: Differentiation**—Develop properties of the six inverse trigonometric functions. Differentiate an inverse trigonometric function. Review the basic differentiation rules for elementary functions.

Teaching Tips

Review pages 373 and 374 of the text to remind students of inverse trigonometric functions. If needed, pass out this information to the class.

Inverse Trigonometric Functions

Recall: How do you find the inverse function of $y = 2x^2 - 1$, $x \geq 0$?

Step 1: Interchange x and y.

$$x = 2y^2 - 1$$

Step 2: Solve for y.

$$x + 1 = 2y^2$$

$$\frac{x + 1}{2} = y^2$$

$$y = \sqrt{\frac{x + 1}{2}}, \quad x \geq 0$$

NOTE: If you were asked to find the inverse function of $y = 2x^2 - 1$, this cannot be done because the domain is not restricted. In other words, it will not pass the Horizontal Line Test.

Also recall the Horizontal Line Test: A function f has an inverse function if any only if no horizontal line intersects the graph of f at more than one point.

Classic examples:

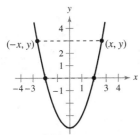

y-axis symmetry

Inverse function DOES NOT exist.

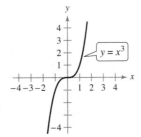

Inverse function DOES exist.

The Inverse Sine Relation

To find the inverse function of $y = \sin x$, interchange x and y to obtain $x = \sin y$. This is the equation of the inverse sine relation.

To graph $x = \sin y$, reflect the graph of $y = \sin x$ about the line $y = x$, which is called the line of reflection as shown below.

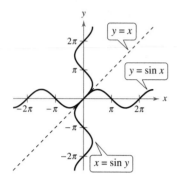

As you can see from the graph, $x = \sin y$ is a relation but not a function as it does not pass the Vertical Line Test. For every value of x in the domain, there are many values of y.

Inverse Trigonometric Functions

In order for the function $y = \sin x$ to have an inverse function, it is necessary to restrict the values that y can assume. Restrict the values using the interval

$$-\frac{\pi}{2} \le y \le \frac{\pi}{2}.$$

The figure below shows the graph of $x = \sin y$ with the restricted interval indicated as a solid line.

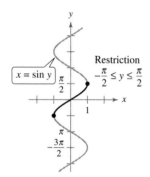

It is apparent from the graph that if $x = \sin y$ is restricted to the interval

$$-\frac{\pi}{2} \le y \le \frac{\pi}{2}$$

then each value of x is associated with exactly one value of y and you have a function rather than just a relation. (That is, on the interval

$$-\frac{\pi}{2} \le y \le \frac{\pi}{2}$$

the graph of $x = \sin y$ is such that no vertical line crosses the curve more than once.) The equation $x = \sin y$, together with the restriction

$$-\frac{\pi}{2} \le y \le \frac{\pi}{2}$$

form the inverse sine function. To designate this function, use the following notation.

62

NOTATION	
The notation used to indicate the **inverse sine function** is as follows:	
Notation	**Meaning**
$y = \sin^{-1} x$ or $y = \arcsin x$	$x = \sin y$ and $-\dfrac{\pi}{2} \le y \le \dfrac{\pi}{2}$

The graphs below show the inverse functions $y = \cos^{-1} x$ and $y = \tan^{-1} x$ and the restrictions that allow them to become functions instead of just relations.

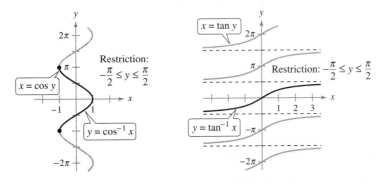

To summarize, here is the definition for the three major inverse trigonometric functions.

Definition: The **inverse trigonometric function** for $y = \sin x$, $y = \cos x$, and $y = \tan x$ are as follows:	
Inverse Function	**Meaning**
$y = \sin^{-1} x$ or $y = \arcsin x$	$x = \sin y$ and $-\dfrac{\pi}{2} \le y \le \dfrac{\pi}{2}$ **In Words:** y is the angle between $-\pi/2$ and $\pi/2$, inclusive, whose sine is x.
$y = \cos^{-1} x$ or $y = \arccos x$	$x = \cos y$ and $0 \le y \le \pi$ **In Words:** y is the angle between 0 and π, inclusive, whose cosine is x.
$y = \tan^{-1} x$ or $y = \arctan x$	$x = \tan y$ and $-\dfrac{\pi}{2} \le y \le \dfrac{\pi}{2}$ **In Words:** y is the angle between $-\pi/2$ and $\pi/2$, inclusive, whose tangent is x.

Use the sample problem below to review the following concepts:

- Definition of inverse function

- Domain and range of the cosine and arccosine functions

- Properties of inverse trigonometric functions

The point $(3\pi/2, 0)$ is on the graph of $y = \cos x$. Does $(0, 3\pi/2)$ lie on the graph of $y = \arccos x$? If not, does this contradict the definition of an inverse function?

Review the definition of inverse function (see page 333), and the domain and range of the cosine (see Appendix C.3) and arccosine functions (see page 374). Note that the point $(3\pi/2, 0)$ lies on the graph of $y = \cos x$, but does not lie on $y = \arccos x$. This does not contradict the definition of an inverse function because the domain of $y = \arccos x$ is $[-1, 1]$ and its range is $[0, \pi]$. Be sure to cover the material at the top of page 375 and the properties of inverse trigonometric functions.

Solution

No, $(0, 3\pi/2)$ is not on the graph of $y = \arccos x$. The domain of $y = \arccos x$ is $[-1, 1]$ and its range is $[0, \pi]$. So, $\arccos(0) = \pi/2$.

How Do You See It? Exercise

Page 380, Exercise 76 The graph of $g(x) = \cos x$ is shown below. Explain whether the points $\left(-\dfrac{1}{2}, \dfrac{2\pi}{3}\right)$, $\left(0, \dfrac{\pi}{2}\right)$, and $\left(\dfrac{1}{2}, -\dfrac{\pi}{3}\right)$ lie on the graph of $y = \arccos x$.

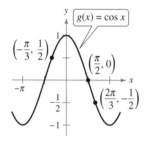

Solution

$\left(-\dfrac{1}{2}, \dfrac{2\pi}{3}\right)$ and $\left(0, \dfrac{\pi}{2}\right)$ lie on the graph of $y = \arccos x$ because both $\dfrac{2\pi}{3}$ and $\dfrac{\pi}{2}$ lie in the interval $[0, \pi]$. $\left(\dfrac{1}{2}, -\dfrac{\pi}{3}\right)$ does not lie on the graph of $y = \arccos x$ because $-\dfrac{\pi}{3}$ is not in the interval $[0, \pi]$.

Suggested Homework Assignment

Pages 379–380: 1, 3, 7–13 odd, 19–35 odd, and 41–61 odd.

Section 5.8 Inverse Trigonometric Functions: Integration

Section Comments

5.8   **Inverse Trigonometric Functions: Integration**—Integrate functions whose antiderivatives involve inverse trigonometric functions. Use the method of completing the square to integrate a function. Review the basic integration rules involving elementary functions.

Teaching Tips

Be sure to go over an example when students must rewrite an integral as a sum of two quotients, as in Example 3 in the text and completing the square as in Example 4.

Review all the basic integration rules on page 385.

Use the sample problem below to review the following concepts:

- Integrating functions whose antiderivatives involve inverse trigonometric functions

- Using the Log Rule for Integration to integrate a rational function

- Rewriting the integrand using the Constant Multiple Rule

Determine which of the integrals can be found using the basic integration formulas you have studied so far in the text.

(a) $\displaystyle\int \frac{1}{1 + x^4}\, dx$ 　　　 (b) $\displaystyle\int \frac{x}{1 + x^4}\, dx$ 　　　 (c) $\displaystyle\int \frac{x^3}{1 + x^4}\, dx$

The integral in part (a) cannot be evaluated using basic integration rules. Have students scan the list of basic integration rules on page 385 to verify this conclusion. $\left(\text{Some students mistakenly believe that the rule of } \displaystyle\int \frac{du}{a^2 + u^2} \text{ applies.}\right)$ The integrals in parts (b) and (c) can be evaluated using the basic integration rules. Part (b) can be evaluated using $\displaystyle\int \frac{du}{a^2 + u^2}$ with $u = x^2$. Part (c) can be evaluated using $\displaystyle\int \frac{du}{u}$ with $u = 1 + x^4$. Note in both cases the use of the Constant Multiple Rule to rewrite the integrand.

Solution

(a) $\displaystyle\int \frac{1}{1 + x^4}\, dx$ cannot be evaluated using the basic integration rules.

(b) $\displaystyle\int \frac{x}{1 + x^4}\, dx = \frac{1}{2}\int \frac{2x}{1 + (x^2)^2}\, dx$

$= \dfrac{1}{2}\arctan(x^2) + C, \quad u = x^2$

(c) $\displaystyle\int \frac{x^3}{1 + x^4}\, dx = \frac{1}{4}\int \frac{4x^3}{1 + x^4}\, dx$

$= \dfrac{1}{4}\ln(1 + x^4) + C, \quad u = 1 + x^4$

65

How Do You See It? Exercise

Page 388, Exercise 54 Using the graph, which value best approximates the area of the region between the x-axis and the function over the interval $\left[-\dfrac{1}{2}, \dfrac{1}{2}\right]$? Explain.

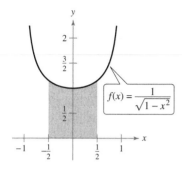

$$f(x) = \frac{1}{\sqrt{1-x^2}}$$

(a) -3 (b) $\dfrac{1}{2}$ (c) 1 (d) 2 (e) 4

Solution

The area is approximately the area of a square of side 1. So, (c) best approximates the area.

Suggested Homework Assignment

Pages 387–388: 1–47 odd and 63.

Section 5.9 Hyperbolic Functions

Section Comments

5.9 **Hyperbolic Functions**—Develop properties of hyperbolic functions. Differentiate and integrate hyperbolic functions. Develop properties of inverse hyperbolic functions. Differentiate and integrate functions involving inverse hyperbolic functions.

Teaching Tips

Use the practice problem below to review the following concept:

- Properties of the hyperbolic functions

Which hyperbolic functions take on only positive values? Which hyperbolic functions are increasing on their domains?

Review the domains and ranges of the hyperbolic functions (see page 391). Note that $y = \cosh x$ and $y = \operatorname{sech} x$ take on only positive values, and $y = \sinh x$ and $y = \tanh x$ are increasing on their domains.

Solution

$f(x) = \cosh x$ and $f(x) = \operatorname{sech} x$ take on only positive values.

$f(x) = \sinh x$ and $f(x) = \tanh x$ are increasing functions.

How Do You See It? Exercise

Page 398, Exercise 64 Use the graphs of f and g shown in the figures to answer the following.

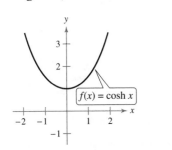
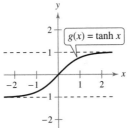

(a) Identify the open interval(s) on which the graphs of f and g are increasing or decreasing.

(b) Identify the open interval(s) on which the graphs of f and g are concave upward or concave downward.

Solution

(a) $f(x) = \cosh x$ is decreasing on $(-\infty, 0)$ and increasing on $(0, \infty)$.

   $g(x) = \tanh x$ is increasing on $(-\infty, \infty)$.

(b) $f(x) = \cosh x$ is concave upward on $(-\infty, \infty)$.

   $g(x) = \tanh x$ is concave upward on $(-\infty, 0)$ and concave downward on $(0, \infty)$.

Suggested Homework Assignment

Pages 397–398: 1–37 odd, 45–59 odd, 65–85 odd, and 91.

Chapter 5 Project

Exponential Growth

The revenue y (in millions of dollars) for Dell Computer Corporation from 1985 through 1993 can be modeled by the equation $y = 42.575(1.707)^x$, where x is the time in years with $x = 0$ corresponding to 1985.

Exercises

1. Use the model $y = 42.575(1.707)^x$ to answer the following questions.

   (a) What was Dell Computer Corporation's revenue in 1985?

   (b) What was Dell Computer Corporation's revenue in 1992?

   (c) In what year was the revenue approximately $3 billion?

2. Find the inverse function of $y = 42.575(1.707)^x$. What does the inverse function represent?

3. Use the inverse function you wrote in Exercise 2 to determine the year when revenue was approximately $3 billion. Compare this to your answer from Exercise 1.

4. Differentiate $y = 42.575(1.707)^x$.

5. What is the rate of change of revenue in 1985? In 1988?

6. Because the revenue follows an exponential growth model, what is true about the revenue's rate of change over time? Explain.

7. Set up a definite integral to determine the total revenue from 1985 through 1993.

8. Evaluate the integral you wrote in Exercise 7 to determine the total revenue from 1985 through 1993.

9. Determine the average monthly revenue from 1985 through 1993.

10. Assuming there are 52 weeks in a year, determine the average weekly revenue from 1985 through 1993.

11. Assuming there are 365 days in a year, determine the average daily revenue from 1985 through 1993.

12. If the revenue continued to follow the same growth model, what would the revenue be in 2006?

13. Based on your answer to Exercise 12, what is the likelihood that the revenue continues to follow this growth model? Explain.

14. Use the Internet to find Dell Computer Corporation's actual revenue in 2006.

15. Based on your findings in Exercises 12 and 14, what conclusions can you make about the growth of the revenue? Does the revenue continue to increase? Does the rate of change continue to increase? Explain.

Chapter 6 Differential Equations

Chapter Comments

Section 6.1 introduces students to the notation and terminology of differential equations. Because solving differential equations analytically can be very difficult, this section considers two other ways of looking at the solution. The first is a slope field, which is a graphical approach. The second is Euler's Method, an approximation technique for initial value problems. Your students should be familiar with all of the ideas in this section.

Be sure to cover Sections 6.2 and 6.3 thoroughly. Here applications involving exponential growth and decay as well as the technique of separation of variables are discussed. This is an excellent opportunity to expose your students to a practical use of the exponential function.

Section 6.4 explores some of the other types of differential equations. You should cover these as time allows. Students frequently become frustrated checking their answers to homework problems involving differential equations. Be sure to point out that there are many correct ways that an answer to a differential equation could be written. As students become more familiar with this work, they will have a better idea of what is expected for an answer.

Section 6.1 Slope Fields and Euler's Method

Section Comments

6.1 **Slope Fields and Euler's Method**—Use initial conditions to find particular solutions of differential equations. Use slope fields to approximate solutions of differential equations. Use Euler's Method to approximate solutions of differential equations.

Teaching Tips

For this section, be sure to explain all basic facts and knowledge students will need for differential equations. Depending on time, you may want to show in general, that every solution to a differential equation is $y = Ce^{-2x}$. Be sure to go over the differences between general and singular solutions. In addition, be sure to illustrate solution curves as done on page 407 and particular solutions and initial conditions. Example 2 is a nice example of finding a particular solution.

How Do You See It? Exercise

Page 414, Exercise 84 The graph shows a solution of one of the following differential equations. Which differential equation was used? Explain your reasoning.

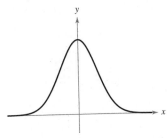

(a) $y' = xy$ (b) $y' = \dfrac{4x}{y}$ (c) $y' = -4xy$ (d) $y' = 4 - xy$

Solution

When $x = 0$, $y' = 0$, therefore (d) is not possible. When $x, y > 0$, $y' < 0$ (decreasing function) therefore (c) is the equation.

Suggested Homework Assignment

Pages 411–414: 1–7 odd, 11, 19, 23, 25, 31, 37, 43, 49, 53, 57, 61, 73, 77, and 87.

Section 6.2 Differential Equations: Growth and Decay

Section Comments

6.2   **Differential Equations: Growth and Decay**—Use separation of variables to solve a simple differential equation. Use exponential functions to model growth and decay in applied problems.

Teaching Tips

The key to this section is not only teaching how to solve differential equations but to see how real-life examples are used. Be sure to go over Examples 2–5 in the text. Other similar problems could be 22, 38, and 56. Stress to students that in this section, the true power of differential equations comes to the forefront through applications.

How Do You See It? Exercise

Page 422, Exercise 60 The functions f and g are both of the form $y = Ce^{kt}$.

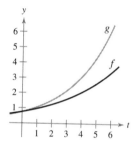

(a) Do the functions f and g represent exponential growth or exponential decay? Explain.

(b) Assume both functions have the same value of C. Which function has a greater value of k? Explain.

Solution

(a) Both functions represent exponential growth because the graphs are increasing.

(b) g has a greater k-value because its graph is increasing at a greater rate than the graph of f.

Suggested Homework Assignment

Pages 420–422: 1–17 odd, 21, 23, 31, 35, 37, 39, 47, 49, 53, and 67.

Section 6.3 Separation of Variables and the Logistic Equation

Section Comments

6.3   **Separation of Variables and the Logistic Equation**—Recognize and solve differential equations that can be solved by separation of variables. Use differential equations to model and solve applied problems. Solve and analyze logistic differential equations.

Teaching Tips

Begin this lecture by having students consider $M(x) + N(y)\dfrac{dy}{dx} = 0$.

70

In order to solve this differential equation, you must use separation of variables. Be sure to go through examples of original differential equations and rewritten differential equations with the separation of variables as done on page 423.

Go through Examples 1–3 or similar problems with the class. Example 4 gives a nice application to wildlife population.

When introducing the logistic equation, ask the class what they believe happens to a population should it follow this model. Then, go through Example 7 or a problem similar.

How Do You See It? Exercise

Page 431, Exercise 68 The growth of a population is modeled by a logistic equation, as shown in the graph below. What happens to the rate of growth as the population increases? What do you think causes this to occur in real-life situations, such as animal or human populations?

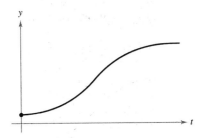

Solution

The rate increases then decreases. *Sample answer:* There might be limits on available food or space.

Suggested Homework Assignment

Pages 429–431: 1–33 odd, 37, 39, 51, 57, 61, 83, and 85.

Section 6.4 First-Order Linear Differential Equations

Section Comments

6.4 **First-Order Linear Differential Equations**—Solve a first-order linear differential equation. Use linear differential equations to solve applied problems.

Teaching Tips

Use the sample problem below to review the following concepts:

- First-order linear differential equations

- Integrating factor

- Derivative of a product

Suppose the expression $u(x)$ is an integrating factor for $y' + P(x)y = Q(x)$. Which of the following is equal to $u'(x)$?

(a) $P(x)u(x)$

(b) $P'(x)u(x)$

(c) $Q(x)u(x)$

(d) $Q'(x)u(x)$

Refer to page 432. In the solution below, note when both sides of the equation are multiplied by the integrating factor $u(x)$, the left-hand side becomes the derivative of a product. So, the derivative of the product is $uy = y' \cdot u + P(x)u \cdot y$. Therefore, $u'(x) = P(x)u$. The answer is (a).

Solution

$y' + P(x)y = Q(x)$

Integrating factor: $u = e^{\int P(x)\,dx}$

$y'u + P(x)yu = Q(x)u$

$\qquad (uy)' = Q(x)u$

So, $u'(x) = P(x)u$.

Answer is (a).

How Do You See It? Exercise

Page 437, Exercise 40 The graph shows the amount of concentrate Q (in pounds) in a solution in a tank at time t (in minutes) as a solution with concentrate enters the tank, is well stirred, and is withdrawn from the tank.

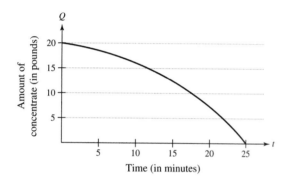

(a) How much concentrate is in the tank at time $t = 0$?

(b) Which is greater, the rate of solution into the tank or the rate of solution withdrawn from the tank? Explain.

(c) At what time is there no concentrate in the tank? What does this mean?

Solution

(a) At $t = 0$, $Q = 20$ pounds.

(b) The rate of solution withdrawn is greater.

(c) At $t = 25$, $Q = 0$. It takes 25 minutes to empty the tank.

Suggested Homework Assignment

Pages 436–438: 1, 3, 9, 17, 23, 27, 31, 33, 37, 51, 53, 55, and 65.

Chapter 6 Project

Finding the Height of a Fall

A detective is investigating a man's death. The man was seen falling from the roof of a building, hitting the ground after 3 seconds. The suspect, who was on the roof with the man, claims the man jumped, but the detective suspects foul play. Assume that acceleration due to gravity is -32 feet per second per second.

Exercises

In Exercises 1–4, the man accidentally fell from the roof.

1. Write a differential equation with initial conditions to model the situation.

2. Solve the differential equation to find the velocity function for the fall.

3. Determine the position function for the fall.

4. Based on the function you wrote in Exercise 3, how tall is the building?

In Exercises 5–8, the man jumped from the roof. Use an initial velocity of 2 feet per second.

5. Write a differential equation with initial conditions to model the situation.

6. Solve the differential equation to find the velocity function for the fall.

7. Determine the position function for the fall.

8. Based on the function you wrote in Exercise 7, how tall is the building?

In Exercises 9–12, the man was pushed off the roof. Use an initial velocity of -3 feet per second.

9. Write a differential equation with initial conditions to model the situation.

10. Solve the differential equation to find the velocity function for the fall.

11. Determine the position function for the fall.

12. Based on the function you wrote in Exercise 11, how tall is the building?

13. What additional information is needed to determine whether foul play was involved?

14. Suppose the building is 144 feet tall. Should the detective suspect foul play? Explain.

15. Suppose the building is more than 144 feet tall. Which of the three scenarios should the detective suspect? Explain.

16. Suppose the building is less than 144 feet tall. Which of the three scenarios should the detective suspect? Explain.

17. The detective discovers that the building is 20 stories tall and each story is about 8 feet. What should the detective conclude?

Chapter 7 Applications of Integration

Chapter Comments

Chapter 7 covers many applications to the definite integral. There are far too many problems in this chapter to cover in a normal calculus course. You would be better off assigning just a few carefully chosen problems from each section covered.

Because you may not have the time to cover each topic in this chapter, you should cover the area between two curves carefully so that students get used to the idea of using a representative rectangle in the given region. Remind students that they are expected to know how to sketch a graph (Chapter 3) and how to find points of intersection (Chapter P).

Both the disk and the shell methods, Sections 7.2 and 7.3, need to be discussed to do a thorough treatment of volumes of solids of revolution. Be sure to go over Examples 3, 4, and 5 of Section 7.3 to convince your students that it is necessary to know both methods.

Arc length, Section 7.4, should be covered because this is built upon in later chapters (Chapters 11 and 13).

Note in Example 3 of Section 7.5 that the weight of the space module is given in metric tons. To convert mile-tons to foot-pounds you need to use the fact that 1 metric ton = 2204.62 pounds.

The remaining topics in this chapter should be covered as time allows. If you prefer to cover applications of integration (Chapter 7) before transcendental functions (Chapter 5), you should postpone covering the following examples and exercises:

Section	Examples	Exercises
7.1	None	27, 28, 35, 36, 39, 41, 42, 45, 46, 48, 56, 63, 64, 78
7.2	None	19, 24, 25, 29, 30, 39, 40, 49–52
7.3	2	28, 30, 36, 46, 59
7.4	4, 5	15–18, 27–29, 33–35, 37, 38, 50, 71
7.5	6	41–44, 48
7.6	None	30
7.7	None	None
Review	N/A	3, 7, 8, 19–21
Problem Solving	N/A	9

Section 7.1 Area of a Region Between Two Curves

Section Comments

7.1 **Area of a Region Between Two Curves**—Find the area of a region between two curves using integration. Find the area of a region between intersecting curves using integration. Describe integration as an accumulation process.

Teaching Tips

Before attempting the exercises, some students may need to review curve sketching (Section 3.6) and how to find points of intersection (Section P.1).

According to the area formula on page 445, $g(x) \le f(x)$ for all x in $[a, b]$. Often, students are confused by the use of $g(x)$ and $f(x)$ in the exercises and simply substitute them into the area formula. When you go over the examples in this section, emphasize the step determining which of the graphs of the two functions lies below the other in the interval of interest.

Use the sample problem below to review the following concept.

- The area of a region between two curves

Use Figure 7.4 on page 445 as you go over the following solution.

Let f and g be continuous functions on $[a, b]$ and let $g(x) \le f(x)$ for all x in $[a, b]$. Write in words the area given by $\int_a^b [f(x) - g(x)]\, dx$. Does the area interpretation of this integral change when $f(x) \ge 0$ and $g(x) \le 0$?

Solution

The integral $\int_a^b [f(x) - g(x)]\, dx$ gives the area of the region bounded by the graphs of f and g ($g(x) \le f(x)$ on $[a, b]$) and the vertical lines $x = a$ and $x = b$. No, the interpretation does not change.

How Do You See It? Exercise

Page 452, Exercise 68 A state legislature is debating two proposals for eliminating the annual budget deficits after 10 years. The rate of decrease of the deficits for each proposal is shown in the figure.

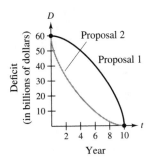

(a) What does the area between the two curves represent?

(b) From the viewpoint of minimizing the cumulative state deficit, which is the better proposal? Explain.

Solution

(a) The area between the two curves represents the difference between the accumulated deficit under the two plans.

(b) Proposal 2 is better because the cumulative deficit (the area under the curve) is less.

Suggested Homework Assignment

Pages 450–453: 1–7 odd, 17, 23, 35, 37–45 odd, 65, 83, and 85.

Section 7.2 Volume: The Disk Method

Section Comments

7.2   **Volume: The Disk Method**—Find the volume of a solid of revolution using the disk method. Find the volume of a solid of revolution using the washer method. Find the volume of a solid with known cross sections.

Teaching Tips

Stress to students that in general, the volume formula is $V = \displaystyle\int_a^b A(x)\, dx$.

Have students consider the following problem:

The region R enclosed by the graphs of $y = x$ and $y = x^2$ is rotated about the x-axis. Find the volume of the resulting solid.

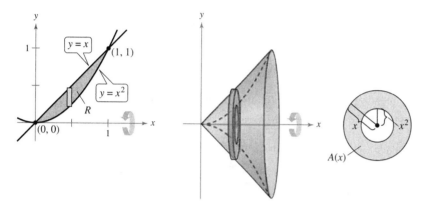

Ask students why it is true that $A(x) = \pi x^2 - \pi(x^2)^2$ instead of $A(x) = \pi(x - x^2)^2$. Lead students to the answer that the cross sections are shaped like concentric circles. The area is the area of the outer disk, πR^2, minus the area of the inner disk, πr^2.

Another good suggested problem to try with the class is:

Find the volume of the solid obtained by rotating the region bounded by $y = 2 - \frac{1}{2}x$ and the x- and y-axes about the x-axis.

Use the sample problem below to review the following concepts:

- The washer method

- The disk method

Identify the integral that represents the volume of the solid obtained by rotating the area between $y = f(x)$ and $y = g(x)$, $a \le x \le b$, about the x-axis. [Assume $f(x) \ge g(x) \ge 0$.]

(a) $\pi \displaystyle\int_a^b [f(x) - g(x)]^2\, dx$ (b) $\pi \displaystyle\int_a^b ([f(x)]^2 - [g(x)]^2)\, dx$

Use an illustration such as Figure 7.19 to show students the relationship between the graphs of $y = f(x)$ and $y = g(x)$. Then go over the disk and washer methods. It should be clear that the answer is (b).

Solution

The answer is (b). See the formula for the washer method, page 457.

76

Page 462, Exercise 56 Use the graph to match the integral for the volume with the axis of rotation.

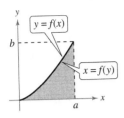

(a) $V = \pi \int_0^b (a^2 - [f(y)]^2)\, dy$ (i) x-axis

(b) $V = \pi \int_a^b (b^2 - [b - f(x)]^2)\, dx$ (ii) y-axis

(c) $V = \pi \int_0^a [f(x)]^2\, dx$ (iii) $x = a$

(d) $V = \pi \int_0^b [a - f(y)]^2\, dy$ (iv) $y = b$

Solution

(a) Matches (ii) because the axis of rotation is vertical, and this is the washer method.

(b) Matches (iv) because the axis of rotation is horizontal, and this is the washer method.

(c) Matches (i) because the axis of rotation is horizontal.

(d) Matches (iii) because the axis of rotation is vertical.

Suggested Homework Assignment

Pages 461–463: 1–15 odd, 17, 23, 25, 31, 37, 39, and 57.

Section 7.3 Volume: The Shell Method

Section Comments

7.3   **Volume: The Shell Method**—Find the volume of a solid of revolution using the shell method. Compare the uses of the disk method and the shell method.

Teaching Tips

Ask students why the factor of 2π appears with cylindrical shells, while π appears with washers. Students should be led to the answer that 2π comes from the volume of a thin cylinder, which is $(2\pi r h)\, dr$, and π comes from the volume of a cross section, which is $\pi r^2\, dr$.

Ask students to set up an integral that computes the volume of the solid generated by rotating the region bounded by the curve $x = -y^3 + y$ and the y-axis about the x-axis.

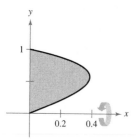

Use the sample problem below to review or to introduce the following concepts:

- Horizontal axis of revolution

- Vertical axis of revolution

Consider the plane region bounded by the graphs of $y = k$, $y = 0$, $x = 0$, and $x = b$, where $k > 0$ and $b > 0$. What are the heights and radii of the cylinders generated when this region is revolved about the (a) x-axis and (b) y-axis.

You can go over this exercise when you introduce the shell method or as you go over the exercises. The simple plane region shown below clearly illustrates the representative rectangles used for a (a) horizontal axis of revolution and (b) vertical axis of revolution.

Solution

(a) radius $= k$

    height $= b$

(b) radius $= b$

    height $= k$

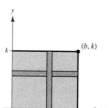

How Do You See It? Exercise

Page 471, Exercise 42 Use the graph to answer the following.

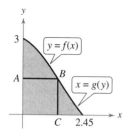

(a) Describe the figure generated by revolving segment AB about the y-axis.

(b) Describe the figure generated by revolving segment BC about the y-axis.

(c) Assume the curve in the figure can be described as $y = f(x)$ or $x = g(y)$ A solid is generated by revolving the region bounded by the curve, $y = 0$, and $x = 0$ about the y-axis. Set up integrals to find the volume of this solid using the disk method and the shell method. (Do not integrate.)

Solution

(a) The figure will be a circle of radius AB and center A.

(b) The figure will be a circular cylinder of radius AB.

(c) Disk method: $V = \pi \displaystyle\int_0^3 [g(y)]^2 \, dy$

Shell method: $V = 2\pi \displaystyle\int_0^{2.45} x f(x) \, dx$

Suggested Homework Assignment

Pages 470–471: 1, 5, 7, 11, 15, 17, 21, 23, 27, 43, and 45.

Section 7.4 Arc Length and Surfaces of Revolution

Section Comments

7.4 **Arc Length and Surfaces of Revolution**—Find the arc length of a smooth curve. Find the area of a surface of revolution.

Teaching Tips

Be sure to derive the definition of arc length from the Distance Formula. Students should have an understanding where the definition comes from and be able to derive this for themselves using logic and mathematical thought.

Ask students why integrals come into play when computing the length of a curve. Lead students to the answer that we are adding up infinitely many quantities, which constitutes integration.

Ask students a multiple-choice question such as: Which of the following integrals gives the length of the graph $y = \sqrt{x}$ between $x = a$ and $x = b$, where $0 < a < b$? You can then provide them with several wrong answers and the correct answer.

For Exercise 36 in this section, be sure students understand that the integral $4\displaystyle\int_0^8 \sqrt{\dfrac{4}{x^{2/3}}} \, dx$ cannot be used to solve this problem because the integrand is not defined on $[0, 8]$. However, using symmetry, the arc length can be found by evaluating $8\displaystyle\int_{2^{3/2}}^8 \sqrt{\dfrac{4}{x^{2/3}}} \, dx$. The lower limit $2^{3/2}$ is the midpoint of the curve on $[0, 8]$, where $y = x$.

Use the sample problem below to review the following concepts:

- Arc length

- Natural logarithmic and natural exponential functions

- Derivatives of natural logarithmic and natural exponential functions

- The number e

Explain why the two integrals are equal.

$$\int_1^e \sqrt{1 + \frac{1}{x^2}} \, dx = \int_0^1 \sqrt{1 + e^{2x}} \, dx$$

Use the integration capabilities of a graphing utility to verify that the integrals are equal.

79

Note that both integrals fit the definition of arc length. In the solution below, note that students need to understand the definitions of natural logarithmic and natural exponential functions and also how to find their derivatives. Students will also need to understand domain, range, and exponentiating both sides of an equation to see that $y = \ln x$ is equivalent to $x = e^y$. After showing the analytical work, the result can be confirmed numerically. If time permits, graph $y = \ln x$ for $1 \le x \le e$ and $x = e^y$ for $0 \le y \le 1$. The graphs on these intervals are equivalent.

Solution

Let $y = \ln x$, $1 \le x \le e$, $y' = \dfrac{1}{x}$, and $s_1 = \displaystyle\int_1^e \sqrt{1 + \dfrac{1}{x^2}}\, dx$.

Equivalently, $x = e^y$, $0 \le y \le 1$, $\dfrac{dx}{dy} = e^y$, and $s_2 = \displaystyle\int_0^1 \sqrt{1 + e^{2y}}\, dy = \displaystyle\int_0^1 \sqrt{1 + e^{2y}}\, dx$.

Numerically, both integrals yield $s = 2.0035$.

How Do You See It? Exercise

Page 482, Exercise 54 The graphs of the functions f_1 and f_2 on the interval $[a, b]$ are shown in the figure. The graph of each function is revolved about the x-axis. Which surface of revolution has the greater surface area? Explain.

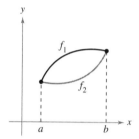

Solution

The surface of revolution given by f_1 will be larger. $r(x)$ is larger for f_1.

Suggested Homework Assignment

Pages 481–483: 1, 3, 7, 13, 15, 17, 19, 23, 27, 33, 39, 45, 57, and 59.

Section 7.5 Work

Section Comments

7.5 **Work**—Find the work done by a constant force. Find the work done by a variable force.

Teaching Tips

Stress to students that work is the integral force over distance.

Ask students to think about a particle moving along the x-axis by a force that measures $6x$ pounds at a point x feet from the origin. Find the work done in moving the particle from the origin to a point 5 feet from the origin. Lead students to the solution of

$$\int_0^5 6x\, dx = 75.$$

Stress to students when going through examples, to draw clear pictures, which emphasizes good problem-solving skills.

80

How Do You See It? Exercise

Page 493, Exercise 40 The graphs show the force F_i (in pounds) required to move an object 9 feet along the x-axis. Order the force functions from the one that yields the least work to the one that yields the most work without doing any calculations. Explain your reasoning.

(a)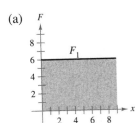

(b)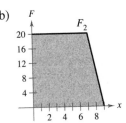

(c)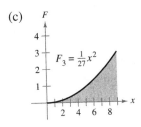

(d)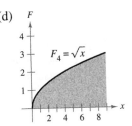

Solution

Because the work equals the area under the force function, you have (c) < (d) < (a) < (b).

Suggested Homework Problems

Pages 491–493: 1, 3, 7, 11, 13, 17, 23, 27, 31, 43, and 47.

Section 7.6 Moments, Centers of Mass, and Centroids

Section Comments

7.6   Moments, Centers of Mass, and Centroids—Understand the definition of mass. Find the center of mass in a one-dimensional system. Find the center of mass in a two-dimensional system. Find the center of mass of a planar lamina. Use the Theorem of Pappus to find the volume of a solid of revolution.

Teaching Tips

Use the sample problem below to review the following concepts:

- Centroid

- Transformations of functions

The centroid of the plane region bounded by the graphs of $y = f(x)$, $y = 0$, $x = 0$, and $x = 1$ is $\left(\frac{5}{6}, \frac{5}{18}\right)$. Is it possible to find the centroid of each of the regions bounded by the graphs of the following sets of equations? If so, identify the centroid and explain your answer.

(a) $y = f(x) + 2$, $y = 2$, $x = 0$, and $x = 1$

(b) $y = f(x - 2)$, $y = 0$, $x = 2$, and $x = 3$

(c) $y = -f(x)$, $y = 0$, $x = 0$, and $x = 1$

(d) $y = f(x)$, $y = 0$, $x = -1$, and $x = 1$

Note the use of transformations in parts (a)–(c): vertical shift upward 2 units, horizontal shift right 2 units, and reflection about the x-axis. These transformations were covered in Section P.3. So, each centroid can be found by applying the transformation to the given centroid as shown below. You do not have enough information to find the centroid in part (d).

Solution

(a) Yes. $(\bar{x}, \bar{y}) = \left(\frac{5}{6}, \frac{5}{18} + 2\right) = \left(\frac{5}{6}, \frac{41}{18}\right)$

(b) Yes. $(\bar{x}, \bar{y}) = \left(\frac{5}{6} + 2, \frac{5}{18}\right) = \left(\frac{17}{6}, \frac{5}{18}\right)$

(c) Yes. $(\bar{x}, \bar{y}) = \left(\frac{5}{6}, -\frac{5}{18}\right)$

(d) No

How Do You See It? Exercise

Page 503, Exercise 44 The centroid of the plane region bounded by the graphs of $y = f(x)$, $y = 0$, $x = 0$, and $x = 3$ is $(1.2, 1.4)$. Without integrating, find the centroid of each of the regions bounded by the graphs of the following sets of equations. Explain your reasoning.

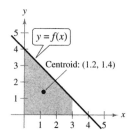

(a) $y = f(x) + 2$, $y = 2$, $x = 0$, and $x = 3$

(b) $y = f(x - 2)$, $y = 0$, $x = 2$, and $x = 5$

(c) $y = -f(x)$, $y = 0$, $x = 0$, and $x = 3$

Solution

(a) Yes. The region is shifted upward two units.

$(\bar{x}, \bar{y}) = (1.2, 1.4 + 2) = (1.2, 3.4)$

(b) Yes. The region is shifted to the right two units.

$(\bar{x}, \bar{y}) = (1.2 + 2, 1.4) = (3.2, 1.4)$

(c) Yes. The region is reflected in the x-axis.

$(\bar{x}, \bar{y}) = (1.2, -1.4)$

Suggested Homework Assignment

Pages 502–503: 1, 3, 7, 9, 11, 15, 23, 31, 35, and 39.

Section 7.7 Fluid Pressure and Fluid Force

Section Comments

7.7   **Fluid Pressure and Fluid Force**—Find fluid pressure and fluid force.

Teaching Tips

For this section, we recommend the use of pictures to motivate a stronger understanding of the applications. Not every application must be covered. We suggest going over Examples 2 and 3 in detail.

How Do You See It? Exercise

Page 510, Exercise 28 Two identical semicircular windows are placed at the same depth in the vertical wall of an aquarium (see figure). Which is subjected to the greater fluid force? Explain.

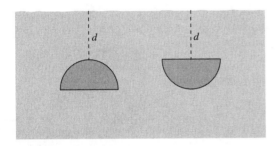

Solution

The left window experiences the greater fluid force because there is more area farther down.

Suggested Homework Assignment

Page 509: 1, 5, 7, 11, 13, 17, 21, and 23.

Chapter 7 Project

Volume and Surface Area of Footballs and Basketballs

A regulation-sized football has the following dimensions:

Length: 11.00–11.25 inches

Girth: 21.25–21.50 inches

A football can be formed by revolving the area under $f(x) = -0.0944x^2 + 3.4$, $-5.5 \leq x \leq 5.5$ about the x-axis.

A regulation-sized basketball is a sphere with a circumference of 29.5 inches. A basketball can be formed by revolving the area under $f(x) = \sqrt{4.7^2 - x^2}$, $-4.7 \leq x \leq 4.7$ about the x-axis.

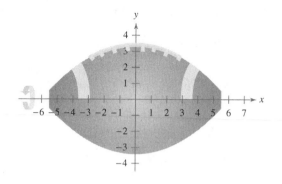

Exercises

1. Use the disk method to set up an integral that gives the volume of a football.

2. Evaluate the integral you wrote in Exercise 1 to approximate the volume of a football.

3. Use the shell method to set up an integral that gives the volume of a football.

4. Evaluate the integral you wrote in Exercise 3 to approximate the volume of a football. Compare this to your answer from Exercise 2.

5. Set up an integral that gives the surface area of a football.

6. Use a graphing utility to evaluate the integral you wrote in Exercise 5 to approximate the surface area of a football.

7. Approximate the volume of a basketball using the formula for the volume of a sphere.

8. Use the disk method to set up an integral that gives the volume of a basketball.

9. Evaluate the integral you wrote in Exercise 8 to approximate the volume of a basketball. Compare this with your answer from Exercise 7.

10. Use the shell method to set up an integral that gives the volume of a basketball.

11. Evaluate the integral you wrote in Exercise 10 to approximate the volume of a basketball. Compare this to your answers from Exercises 7 and 9.

12. Approximate the surface area of a basketball using the formula for the surface area of a sphere.

13. Set up an integral that gives the surface area of a basketball.

14. Use a graphing utility to evaluate the integral you wrote in Exercise 13 to approximate the surface area of a basketball. Compare this to your answer from Exercise 12.

Chapter 8 Integration Techniques and Improper Integrals

Chapter Comments

This chapter and the following one will require a lot of time to cover. Be prepared to use two class days for most of the sections in this chapter. The first section is a review of all of the integration covered up to this point. Your students should have memorized the list of basic integration rules found on page 516. In addition to these basic rules, this section reviews techniques necessary for integration, such as completing the square. Be sure to go over each of the examples in this section.

When you cover integration by parts in Section 8.2, be sure to find one of the integrals $\int \sec^3 x \, dx$ or $\int \csc^3 x \, dx$. It is important to point out that "parts" is the way to integrate $\int \sec^m x \, dx$, where m is positive and odd.

Sections 8.3 and 8.4 may be difficult for students who do not have their trigonometry memorized. Insist that they learn it and deduct points when the trigonometry is not correct. In Section 8.4, do some problems converting the limits of integration when a new variable is introduced into the problem, such as Example 4 on page 544.

Section 8.5 will take two days to cover because most students will need help reviewing how to find partial fractions and how to solve simultaneous equations. Choose your in-class examples carefully in order to review these techniques. Spend the first day on linear factors and the second day working with the quadratic factors.

To introduce the approximation techniques of Simpson's Rule and the Trapezoidal Rule, present an integral problem for which there is no antiderivative that is an elementary function, such as $\int_{\pi/4}^{\pi/2} \sin^2 x \, dx$. This is a good opportunity to convince your students that not all functions have antiderivatives that are elementary functions. If you are pressed for time, the development of Simpson's Rule could be eliminated, but not the rule itself.

In addition to integration by tables, Section 8.7 covers the technique for integrating rational functions of sine and cosine (page 569). This technique is interesting and worth doing, but do not dwell on it.

Section 8.8 incorporates the ideas of L'Hôpital's Rule.

Section 8.1 Basic Integration Rules

Section Comments

8.1   **Basic Integration Rules**—Review procedures for fitting an integrand to one of the basic integration rules.

Teaching Tips

This section provides a great way for the instructor to emphasize many integration techniques. Here are some suggested problems to cover with students:

$$\int x^3 \sqrt{1 - x^2} \, dx \qquad \int e^{x^{1/2}} \, dx \qquad \int (x \ln x)^2 \, dx \qquad \int \frac{1}{x^2 + 4} \, dx$$

Be sure to review Exercise 33. Also, be sure to cover Example 4 on page 518 and the technique discussed in the remark after Example 4.

Be sure to go over Exercises 23, 35, and 43. Be sure to explain the procedures for fitting integrands to basic rules on page 519. Of course, your students should memorize the list of basic integration rules on page 516.

Use the sample problem below to review the following concepts:

- Verifying that two forms of an antiderivative are equivalent

- Using properties of exponents to rewrite an expression

- Using trigonometric identities to rewrite an expression

(a) Explain why the antiderivative of $y_1 = e^{x+C_1}$ is equivalent to the antiderivative of $y_2 = Ce^x$.

(b) Explain why the antiderivative of $y_1 = \sec^2 x + C_1$ is equivalent to the antiderivative of $y_2 = \tan^2 x + C$.

Use the solution below. Part (a) uses a property of exponents $(a^m a^n = a^{m+n})$. Be sure students understand that e^{C_1} is a constant. Part (b) uses the trigonometric identity $\sec^2 x = \tan^2 x + 1$. Be sure students understand that $1 + C_1 = C$.

Solution

(a) They are equivalent because $e^{x+C_1} = e^x \cdot e^{C_1} = Ce^x$, $C = e^{C_1}$.

(b) They differ by a constant.

$$\sec^2 x + C_1 = (\tan^2 x + 1) + C_1 = \tan^2 x + C$$

How Do You See It? Exercise

Page 522, Exercise 86 Using the graph, is $\displaystyle\int_0^5 f(x)\,dx$ positive or negative? Explain.

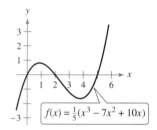

$f(x) = \frac{1}{5}(x^3 - 7x^2 + 10x)$

Solution

$\displaystyle\int_0^5 f(x)\,dx < 0$ because there is more area below the x-axis than above.

Suggested Homework Assignment

Pages 520–521: 1, 5–45 odd, and 57–73 odd.

Section 8.2 Integration by Parts

Section Comments

8.2   Integration by Parts—Find an antiderivative using integration by parts.

Teaching Tips

Start this lesson by emphasizing that every differentiation rule has a corresponding integration rule. The substitution rule for integration corresponds to the Chain Rule for differentiation. The rule that corresponds to the Product Rule for differentiation is called the rule for integration by parts.

The Product Rule states that if f and g are differentiable functions, then

$$\frac{d}{dx}[f(x)g(x)] = f(x)g'(x) + g(x)f'(x)$$

In the notation for indefinite integrals this equation becomes

$$\int [f(x)g'(x) + g(x)f'(x)]\, dx = f(x)g(x)$$

or

$$\int f(x)g'(x)\, dx + \int g(x)f'(x)\, dx = f(x)g(x)$$

Rearrange this equation as

$$\int f(x)g'(x)\, dx = f(x)g(x) - \int g(x)f'(x)\, dx$$

This is called the formula for integration by parts. It is perhaps easier to remember using the following notation. Let $u = f(x)$ and $v = g(x)$. Then the differentials are $du = f'(x)\, dx$ and $dv = g'(x)\, dx$. So, by the Substitution Rule, the formula for integration by parts is:

$$\int u\, dv = uv - \int v\, du$$

A good mnemonic to give the class is LATE: logarithmic, algebraic, trigonometric, and exponential. The first function that appears in LATE will be the u, the second will be the dv. For example, using $\int xe^x\, dx$, $u = x$ as an algebraic function is the first function to appear using LATE and $dv = e^x\, dx$ should be the next as an exponential function appears next.

In general this trick works. However, you should stress that this does not work for all integrals.

For example, in the integral $\int_0^1 \tan^{-1} x\, dx$, you should let $u = \tan^{-1} x$ and $dv = dx$.

Be sure to go over a problem such as $\int e^x \sin x\, dx$ so that students realize there is a pattern.

Exercises 5–10 give students practice identifying u and dv for finding an integral using integration by parts, but students do not have to evaluate the integral.

Present Exercise 61 to review the following concepts:

- Integration by parts

- u-substitution

- Summary of common integrals using integration by parts

Use integration by parts to evaluate each integral in (b), (c), and (e). Note in part (e) that substitution also works.

For the integrals in (a), (d), and (f), use substitution as follows.

(a) Use substitution by letting $u = \ln x$ and $du = \dfrac{1}{x}\, dx$.

(d) Use substitution by letting $u = x^2$ and $du = 2x\, dx$.

(f) Use substitution by letting $u = x^2 + 1$ and $du = 2x\, dx$.

Solution

(a) No
   Substitution

(b) Yes
   $u = \ln x,\ dv = x\,dx$

(c) Yes
   $u = x^2,\ dv = e^{-3x}\,dx$

(d) No
   Substitution

(e) Yes

   $u = x,\ dv = \dfrac{1}{\sqrt{x+1}}\,dx$

   $\left(\text{Substitution also works. Let } u = \sqrt{x+1}.\right)$

(f) No
   Substitution

How Do You See It? Exercise

Page 530, Exercise 62 Use the graph of f' shown in the figure to answer the following.

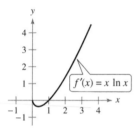

(a) Approximate the slope of f at $x = 2$. Explain.

(b) Approximate any open intervals in which the graph of f is increasing and any open intervals on which it is decreasing. Explain.

Solution

(a) The slope of f at $x = 2$ is approximately 1.4 because $f'(2) \approx 1.4$

(b) $f' < 0$ on $(0, 1) \rightarrow f$ is decreasing on $(0, 1)$.

   $f' > 0$ on $(1, \infty) \rightarrow f$ is increasing on $(1, \infty)$.

Suggested Homework Assignment

Pages 529–531: 1, 3, 11–33 odd, 43–51 odd, 55, 83, and 85.

Section 8.3 Trigonometric Integrals

Section Comments

8.3   **Trigonometric Integrals**—Solve trigonometric integrals involving powers of sine and cosine. Solve trigonometric integrals involving powers of secant and tangent. Solve trigonometric integrals involving sine-cosine products.

88

Teaching Tips

This section and the next section may be difficult for students who do not have their trigonometry memorized. The product-to-sum formulas are given on page 537. We also note the importance of the half-angle formulas in part 3 of the guidelines on page 532. A longer list of identities is given on page C19 in Appendix C.3.

Start out the lesson by asking students, when m is odd, can you integrate $\int \sin^m x \, dx$ by letting $u = \cos x$. Why does m have to be odd for this to work?

Lead students to the answer that when m is odd, you can write $\sin^m x \, dx$ as $(1 - \cos^2 x)^{(m-1)/2} \sin x \, dx$, and then substitution works. If m is even, then $(m - 1)/2$ is not an integer.

Other suggested problems to do with the class are:

$$\int \sin^4 x \cos^3 x \, dx, \qquad \int \sin^7 x \sqrt[3]{\cos x} \, dx, \qquad \text{and} \qquad \int \sin^2 x \cos^4 x \, dx.$$

Review the strategies for evaluating $\int \sin^m x \cos^n x \, dx$:

1. If m or n is odd, save one power of the $\sin x$ or $\cos x$ and use the Pythagorean Identity: $\sin^2 x + \cos^2 x = 1$.

2. If m or n are both even, use the half-angle formulas.

You may also want to find $\int \sqrt{\tan x} \sec^4 x \, dx$ to illustrate the cases of $\int \tan^m x \sec^n x \, dx$.

Use the sample problem below to review or to introduce the following concepts:

- Integrals involving powers of sine and cosine

- Integrals involving powers of secant and tangent

For each pair of integrals, determine which one is more difficult to evaluate. Explain your reasoning.

(a) $\displaystyle\int \sin^{372} x \cos x \, dx$ $\qquad\qquad$ $\displaystyle\int \sin^4 x \cos^4 x \, dx$

(b) $\displaystyle\int \tan^{400} x \sec^2 x \, dx$ $\qquad\qquad$ $\displaystyle\int \tan^{400} x \sec x \, dx$

In part (a), the first integral can be integrated by letting $u = \sin x$ and $du = \cos x \, dx$. Then apply the Power Rule and integrate as shown below. The second integral would require you to use a half-angle identity and then convert the integrand to odd powers of cosine. So, the first integral is easier to evaluate than the second one.

In part (b), the first integral can be integrated by letting $u = \tan x$ and $du = \sec^2 x \, dx$. Then apply the Power Rule and integrate as shown below. The second integral is more difficult to evaluate because it doesn't fit any of the guidelines for evaluating integrals involving powers of secant and tangent, and it is difficult to try to convert to sines and cosines.

Solution

(a) The second one is more difficult. The first one is easy: $\displaystyle\int \sin^{372} x \cos x \, dx = \dfrac{\sin^{373} x}{373} + C$

(b) The second one is more difficult. The first one is easy: $\displaystyle\int \tan^{400} x \sec^2 x \, dx = \dfrac{\tan^{401} x}{401} + C$

How Do You See It? Exercise

Page 539, Exercise 70 Use the graph of f' shown in the figure to answer the following.

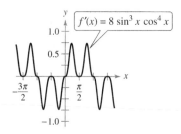

$f'(x) = 8 \sin^3 x \cos^4 x$

(a) Using the interval shown in the graph, approximate the value(s) of x where f is maximum. Explain.

(b) Using the interval shown in the graph, approximate the value(s) of x where f is minimum. Explain.

Solution

(a) f has a maximum at the points where f' changes from positive to negative: $x = -\pi, \pi$.

(b) f has a minimum at the points where f' changes from negative to positive: $x = 0$.

Suggested Homework Assignment

Pages 538–539: 1, 3–15 odd, 21–33 odd, 43, 59–65 odd, and 75.

Section 8.4 Trigonometric Substitution

Section Topics

8.4   **Trigonometric Substitution**—Use trigonometric substitution to find an integral. Use integrals to model and solve real-life applications.

Teaching Tips

This section may be difficult for the students who do not have their trigonometry memorized. See the note at the beginning of Section 8.3 for more details.

Ask students why you should use the trigonometric substitution of $x = \tan \theta$ when the term $1 + x^2$ appears. How could this make things easier? Lead students to the answer that you can use the Pythagorean Identity $\tan^2 x + 1 = \sec^2 x$.

We suggest using Exercise 45 to review the following concepts:

- Trigonometric substitution

- u-substitution

- Partial fraction decomposition and integrals (previews next section)

In addition, use this problem as part (c): Evaluate the integral $\displaystyle\int \frac{4}{4 - x^2}\, dx$ using trigonometric

substitution. Then evaluate using the identity $\dfrac{4}{4 - x^2} = \left(\dfrac{1}{x + 2} - \dfrac{1}{x - 2}\right)$. Discuss the results.

The graphs shown on the next page in parts (a) and (c) are provided on transparencies. Note that the identity used in part (c) is the partial fraction decomposition of the rational function given in the integrand. If you have time to go over this, you can use it to preview Section 8.5 without doing the partial fraction decomposition or using the terminology.

Solution

(a) u-substitution: Let $u = 1 - x^2$, $du = -2x\,dx$.

$$\int \frac{x}{\sqrt{1 - x^2}}\,dx = -\frac{1}{2}\int (1 - x^2)^{-1/2}\,(-2x)\,dx$$

$$= -\frac{1}{2}(1 - x^2)^{1/2}(2) + C = -\sqrt{1 - x^2} + C$$

Trigonometric substitution:

Let $x = \sin\theta$, $dx = \cos\theta\,d\theta$, $a = 1$, $\sqrt{1 - x^2} = \cos\theta$.

$$\int \frac{x}{\sqrt{1 - x^2}}\,dx = \int \frac{\sin\theta}{\cos\theta}\cos\theta\,d\theta = \int \sin\theta\,d\theta$$

$$= -\cos\theta + C = -\sqrt{1 - x^2} + C$$

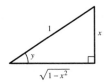

The answers are equivalent.

(b) $\displaystyle\int \frac{x^2}{x^2 + 9}\,dx = \int \frac{x^2 + 9 - 9}{x^2 + 9}\,dx = \int \left(1 - \frac{9}{x^2 + 9}\right)dx = x - 3\arctan\left(\frac{x}{3}\right) + C$

Let $x = 3\tan\theta$, $x^2 + 9 = 9\sec^2\theta$, $dx = 3\sec^2\theta\,d\theta$.

$$\int \frac{x^2}{x^2 + 9}\,dx = \int \frac{9\tan^2\theta}{9\sec^2\theta}\,3\sec^2\theta\,d\theta$$

$$= 3\int \tan^2\theta\,d\theta = 3\int (\sec^2\theta - 1)\,d\theta$$

$$= 3\tan\theta - 3\theta + C_1$$

$$= x - 3\arctan\left(\frac{x}{3}\right) + C_1$$

The answers are equivalent.

(c) $x = 2\sin\theta$, $dx = 2\cos\theta\,d\theta$, $4 - x^2 = 4\cos^2\theta$

$$\int \frac{4}{4 - x^2}\,dx = \int \frac{4 \cdot 2\cos\theta}{4\cos^2\theta}\,d\theta = 2\int \sec\theta\,d\theta$$

$$= 2\ln|\sec\theta + \tan\theta| + C$$

$$= 2\ln\left|\frac{2}{\sqrt{4 - x^2}} + \frac{x}{\sqrt{4 - x^2}}\right| + C$$

$$= \ln\left|\frac{2 + x}{\sqrt{(2 + x)(2 - x)}}\right|^2 + C = \ln\left|\frac{2 + x}{2 - x}\right| + C$$

$$\int \frac{4}{4 - x^2}\,dx = \int \left(\frac{1}{x + 2} - \frac{1}{x - 2}\right)dx = \ln|x + 2| - \ln|x - 2| + C = \ln\left|\frac{x + 2}{x - 2}\right| + C$$

The answers are equivalent.

How Do You See It? Exercise

Page 548, Exercise 46 Use the graph of f' shown in the figure to answer the following.

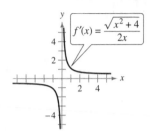

(a) Identify the open interval(s) on which the graph of f is increasing or decreasing. Explain.

(b) Identify the open interval(s) on which the graph of f is concave upward or concave downward. Explain.

Solution

(a) The graph of f is increasing when $f' > 0$: $0 < x < \infty$.

   The graph of f is decreasing when $f' < 0$: $-\infty < x < 0$.

(b) The graph of f is concave upward when the graph of f' is increasing. There are no such intervals.

   The graph of f is concave downward when the graph of f' is decreasing: $-\infty < x < 0$ and $0 < x < \infty$.

Suggested Homework Assignment

Page 547: 1–41 odd.

Section 8.5 Partial Fractions

Section Comments

8.5   **Partial Fractions**—Understand the concept of a partial fraction decomposition. Use partial fraction decomposition with linear factors to integrate rational functions. Use partial fraction decomposition with quadratic factors to integrate rational functions.

Teaching Tips

Students need help finding partial fractions and with solving simultaneous equations. In addition to going over the examples in this section, students that need more help should review Section 7.4 of *Precalculus*, 10th edition, by Larson.

Ask students why you would want to write $\dfrac{1}{(x + 1)(x + 3)}$ as the sum of two fractions. Lead students to the answer that it is much easier to find $\displaystyle\int \dfrac{1}{x + 1}\,dx$ and $\displaystyle\int \dfrac{1}{x + 3}\,dx$ than it is to find $\displaystyle\int \dfrac{1}{(x + 1)(x + 3)}\,dx$.

Ask students to recall how to find $\displaystyle\int \dfrac{A}{x + a}\,dx$ and $\displaystyle\int \dfrac{B}{(x + a)^2}\,dx$. You may also wish to find

$\displaystyle\int \dfrac{dx}{x^2 + 2x + 6} = \int \dfrac{dx}{(x + 1)^2 + 5}$. Remind students how to divide polynomials using long division

such as $\dfrac{2x^3 - 9x^2 + 14x + 5}{x - 3}$ and rewriting this as $2x^2 + 15x + 59 + \dfrac{182}{x - 3}$, and then to find

$\displaystyle\int \dfrac{2x^3 + 9x^2 + 14x + 5}{x - 3}\,dx.$

92

Be sure to tell the class that in order to use partial fractions, the degree of the numerator must be less than the degree of the denominator. So, to find $\int \dfrac{x^4 + 2}{x^2 - 1} \, dx$, you first must perform long division and rewrite the integral as $\int \left(x^2 + 1 + \dfrac{3}{x^2 - 1} \right) dx$.

Be sure to go over how to find the coefficients for a partial fraction decomposition in two different ways: (1) Use linear equations and (2) use the method of creating zeros.

Go over the process of partial fractions for quadratic terms as in $\dfrac{4}{(x^2 + 3)(x - 1)}$.

Go over the process of partial fractions for products of powers of linear terms.

Be sure to review that a quadratic in the denominator of $f(x) = \dfrac{1}{x^2 + 5x + 6}$ is reducible. It can be factored into two linear terms $x + 2$ and $x + 3$ and so, the partial fraction decomposition is found by writing $\dfrac{1}{x^2 + 5x + 6} = \dfrac{A}{x + 2} + \dfrac{B}{x + 3}$ and solving for A and B.

Show students how a complicated partial fractions problem would be set up without trying to solve it. A sample problem could be: $\int \dfrac{5x + 3}{x^3(x + 1)(x^2 + x + 4)(x^2 + 3)} \, dx$.

Work through examples where partial fractions are NOT needed. For example: $\int \dfrac{4x + 3}{2x^2 + 3x + 4} \, dx$.

Use Exercises 37–39 to review the following concepts:

- u-substitution

- Completing the square

- Partial fractions

- Arctangent rule

Solution

For the integral in Exercise 37, use substitution with $u = x^2 + 2x - 8$ and $du = (2x + 2) \, dx$. Then apply the Log Rule.

For the integral in Exercise 38, use partial fractions to rewrite the integrand as $\dfrac{4}{x + 4} + \dfrac{3}{x - 2}$, write the integral as the sum of two integrals, and then apply the Log Rule.

For the integral in Exercise 39, rewrite the integral as $4 \int \dfrac{1}{(x + 1)^2 + 4} \, dx$ and then apply the Arctangent Rule with $u = x + 1$ and $a = 2$. (Note that the denominator is rewritten by completing the square.)

How Do You See It? Exercise

Page 557, Exercise 40 Use the graph of f' shown in the figure to answer the following.

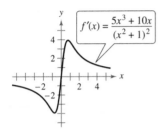

$$f'(x) = \frac{5x^3 + 10x}{(x^2 + 1)^2}$$

(a) Is $f(3) - f(2) > 0$? Explain.

(b) Which is greater, the area under the graph of f' from 1 to 2, or the area under the graph of f' from 3 to 4?

Solution

(a) Yes. Because $f' > 0$ on $(0, 5)$, f is increasing, and $f(3) > f(2)$. Therefore, $f(3) - f(2) > 0$.

(b) The area under the graph of f' is greater on the interval $[1, 2]$ because the graph is decreasing on $[1, 4]$.

Suggested Homework Assignment

Pages 557–558: 1–31 odd and 41.

Section 8.6 Numerical Integration

Section Comments

8.6 **Numerical Integration**—Approximate a definite integral using the Trapezoidal Rule. Approximate a definite integral using Simpson's Rule. Analyze the approximate errors in the Trapezoidal Rule and Simpson's Rule.

Teaching Tips

After stating the Trapezoidal, Midpoint, and Simpson's Rules, ask students where these rules would be needed in the real world. Any answer that involves a discrete rate of change is acceptable.

Use the following sample problem:

The function f is continuous on the closed interval $[2, 10]$ and has the values given below. Using the subintervals $[2, 6]$, $[6, 7]$, and $[7, 10]$, what is the trapezoidal approximation of $\int_2^{10} f(x)\, dx$?

x	2	6	7	10
$f(x)$	5	15	17	11

You may wish to talk about and illustrate the geometry behind each rule for this section.

How Do You See It? Exercise

Page 565, Exercise 38 The function f is concave upward on the interval $[0, 2]$ and the function g is concave downward on the interval $[0, 2]$, as shown in the figure.

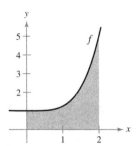 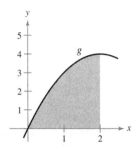

(a) Using the Trapezoidal Rule with $n = 4$, which integral would be overestimated, $\int_0^2 f(x)\, dx$ or $\int_0^2 g(x)\, dx$? Which integral would be underestimated? Explain your reasoning.

(b) Which rule would you use for more accurate approximations of $\int_0^2 f(x)\, dx$ and $\int_0^2 g(x)\, dx$, the Trapezoidal Rule or Simpson's Rule? Explain your reasoning.

Solution

(a) The integral $\int_0^2 f(x)\, dx$ would be overestimated because the trapezoids would be above the curve. Similarly, the integral $\int_0^2 g(x)\, dx$ would be underestimated.

(b) Simpson's Rule would be more accurate because it takes into account the curvature of the graph.

Suggested Homework Assignment

Page 564: 1, 3, 9, 17, 21, 25, 29, and 37.

Section 8.7 Integration by Tables and Other Integration Techniques

Section Comments

8.7   **Integration by Tables and Other Integration Techniques**—Find an indefinite integral using a table of integrals. Find an indefinite integral using reduction formulas. Find an indefinite integral involving rational functions of sine and cosine.

Teaching Tips

Begin this lesson asking students if they can find an antiderivative of $F(x) = \sqrt{x^3 + 1}$ and $G(x) = e^{x^2}$. Lead students to realize that the answer for each function is no. Stress to students that there are many situations where you can't find an antiderivative. You can approximate areas under these curves using one of the three numeric integration approximations studied so far using the Midpoint, Simpson's, or the Trapezoidal Rules.

However, can you find $\int \sqrt{50x - x^2}\, dx$ using the table of integrals? In this case, yes.

If given $\displaystyle\int \frac{x^2}{\sqrt{19 - 16x^2}}\, dx$, you can rewrite $\dfrac{x^2}{\sqrt{19 - 16x^2}}$ as $\dfrac{x^2}{4\sqrt{\frac{19}{16} - x^2}}$ and then use a table of integrals to solve this problem without using substitution. You can use a trigonometric substitution of $x = \dfrac{\sqrt{19}}{4}\sin\theta$ to complete this problem.

Another good sample problem to present to students is

$$\int \frac{x^2 + 3x + 1}{\sqrt{x^2 - 4}}\, dx = \int \frac{x^2}{\sqrt{x^2 - 4}}\, dx + \int \frac{3x}{\sqrt{x^2 - 4}}\, dx + \int \frac{1}{\sqrt{x^2 - 4}}\, dx.$$

Point out that two out of the three integrals above can be solved using the table of integrals and the other can be solved using substitution.

Use Exercise 66 to review the following concepts:

- Integration by tables

- *u*-substitution

- Log Rule

- Arctangent Rule

- Integration by parts

As you go over the solution, review the formula or method as much as you think is necessary. As students do more integration problems, they should be getting a better sense of what methods to use.

Solution

(a) Arctangent formula, Formula 23: $\int \frac{1}{u^2 + 1}\, du, \; u = e^x$

(b) Log Rule: $\int \frac{1}{u}\, du, \; u = e^x + 1$

(c) Substitution: $u = x^2$, $du = 2x\, dx$, then Formula 81

(d) Integration by parts

(e) Cannot be integrated.

(f) Formula 16 with $u = e^{2x}$

How Do You See It? Exercise

Page 571, Exercise 70 Use the graph of f' shown in the figure to answer the following.

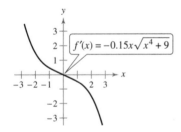

$$f'(x) = -0.15x\sqrt{x^4 + 9}$$

(a) Approximate the slope of f at $x = -1$. Explain.

(b) Approximate any open intervals in which the graph of f is increasing and any open intervals in which it is decreasing. Explain.

Solution

(a) The slope of f at $x = -1$ is approximately 0.5 ($f' > 0$ at $x = -1$).

(b) $f' > 0$ on $(-\infty, 0)$, so f is increasing on $(-\infty, 0)$.

   $f' < 0$ on $(0, \infty)$, so f is decreasing on $(0, \infty)$.

Suggested Homework Assignment

Pages 570–571: 1–47 odd, 55–61 odd, and 63.

Section 8.8 Improper Integrals

Section Comments

8.8   **Improper Integrals**—Evaluate an improper integral that has an infinite limit of integration. Evaluate an improper integral that has an infinite discontinuity.

Teaching Tips

As a motivating example, ask students why $\displaystyle\int_1^6 \frac{dx}{x^2 - 3}$ is an improper integral. Lead students to the answer that the integrand is not defined for $x = \sqrt{3}$.

Ask students to consider the infinite region S that lies under the curve $y = 1/x^2$, above the x-axis, and to the right of the line $x = 1$. Students may think that since S is infinite, its area must be infinite. The area of the part of S that lies to the left of the line $x = t$ is

$$A(t) = \int_1^t \frac{1}{x^2}\,dx = -\frac{1}{x}\bigg|_1^t = 1 - \frac{1}{t}.$$

Notice that $A(t) < 1$ no matter how large t is chosen.

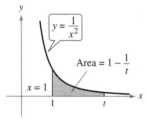

We also observe that $\displaystyle\lim_{t\to\infty} A(t) = \lim_{t\to\infty}\left(1 - \frac{1}{t}\right) = 1.$

The area of the shaded region approaches 1 as t approaches infinity, and so the area of the infinite region S is equal to 1:

$$\int_1^\infty \frac{1}{x^2}\,dx = \lim_{t\to\infty}\int_1^t \frac{1}{x^2}\,dx = 1$$

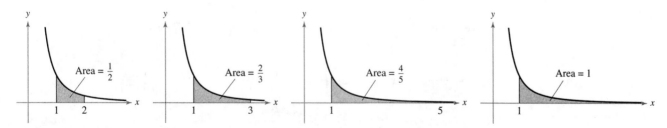

You can now state the first part of the definition of an improper integral.

Stress to students that any improper integral in the first part of the definition can be interpreted as an area provided that f is a positive function. For example, if $f(x) \geq 0$ and the integral $\int_a^\infty f(x)\, dx$ is convergent, then define the area of the region:

$S = \{(x, y) | x \geq a, 0 \leq y \leq f(x)\}$ in the figure below to be $A(S) = \int_a^\infty f(x)\, dx$.

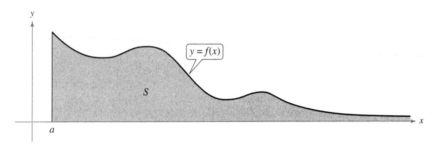

This is correct since $\int_a^\infty f(x)\, dx$ is the limit as t approaches infinity of the area under the graph of f from a to t.

Perform a divergent example such as $\int_1^\infty \dfrac{1}{x}\, dx$.

$$\int_1^\infty \frac{1}{x}\, dx = \lim_{t \to \infty} \int_1^t \frac{1}{x}\, dx$$

$$= \lim_{t \to \infty} \ln|x| \Big|_1^t$$

$$= \lim_{t \to \infty} (\ln t - \ln 1)$$

$$= \lim_{t \to \infty} \ln t$$

$$= \infty$$

The limit does not exist as a finite number and so the improper integral $\int_1^\infty \dfrac{1}{x}\, dx$ is divergent.

Other examples to consider working out with the students are: $\displaystyle\int_0^{\sqrt{2}} \frac{dx}{\sqrt{2 - x^2}}$ and $\displaystyle\int_1^3 \frac{dx}{x^2 - 2}$.

Note that $\displaystyle\int_1^3 \frac{dx}{x^2 - 2}$ converges if and only if $\displaystyle\int_1^{\sqrt{2}} \frac{dx}{x^2 - 2}$ and $\displaystyle\int_{\sqrt{2}}^3 \frac{dx}{x^2 - 2}$, but ask why $\displaystyle\int_1^3 \frac{dx}{x^2 - 2}$ diverges.

Stress the importance of Theorem 8.7 by doing Example 11 in the text.

Work out the following exercise with the class to review the following concepts:

- Improper integral

- Infinite discontinuity

For each integral, find a nonnegative real number b that makes the integral improper. Explain your reasoning.

(a) $\displaystyle\int_0^b \frac{1}{x^2 - 9}\, dx$ (b) $\displaystyle\int_0^b \frac{1}{\sqrt{4 - x}}\, dx$ (c) $\displaystyle\int_0^b \frac{x}{x^2 - 7x + 12}\, dx$

(d) $\displaystyle\int_b^{10} \ln x\, dx$ (e) $\displaystyle\int_0^b \tan 2x\, dx$ (f) $\displaystyle\int_0^b \frac{\cos x}{1 - \sin x}\, dx$

98

Some students may provide answers where b is ∞. Remind students that ∞ and $-\infty$ do not denote real numbers. The symbols ∞ and $-\infty$ simply are ways to describe unbounded conditions more concisely. Note that some of the integrands have two or more infinite discontinuities, so answers other than those shown below are possible.

Solution

(a) $b = 3$ (infinite discontinuity at 3)

(b) $b = 4$ (infinite discontinuity at 4)

(c) $b = 3$ (or $b = 4$) (infinite discontinuity at 3)

(d) $b = 0$ (infinite discontinuity at 0)

(e) $b = \dfrac{\pi}{4}$ $\left(\text{infinite discontinuity at } \dfrac{\pi}{4}\right)$

(f) $b = \dfrac{\pi}{2}$ $\left(\text{infinite discontinuity at } \dfrac{\pi}{2}\right)$

How Do You See It? Exercise

Page 581, Exercise 76 The graph shows the probability density function for a car brand that has a mean fuel efficiency of 26 miles per gallon and a standard deviation of 2.4 miles per gallon.

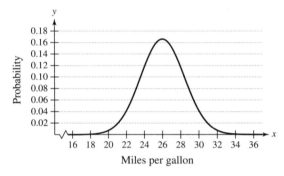

(a) Which is greater, the probability of choosing a car at random that gets between 26 and 28 miles per gallon or the probability of choosing a car at random that gets between 22 and 24 miles per gallon?

(b) Which is greater, the probability of choosing a car at random that gets between 20 and 22 miles per gallon or the probability of choosing a car at random that gets at least 30 miles per gallon?

Solution

(a) The area under the curve is greater on the interval $26 \le x \le 28$ than on the interval $22 \le x \le 24$. So, the probability is greater for choosing a car getting between 26 and 28 miles per gallon.

(b) The area under the curve is greater on the interval $x \ge 30$ than on the interval $20 \le x \le 22$. So, the probability is greater for choosing a car getting at least 30 miles per gallon.

Suggested Homework Assignment

Pages 579–580: 1–47 odd, 53–57 odd, and 69.

Chapter 8 Project

Using Derivatives to Integrate

Repeated integration by parts can be used to show that

$$\int \cos(Ax)e^{Bx}\, dx = De^{Bx}\cos(Ax) + Fe^{Bx}\sin(Ax) + C$$

and

$$\int \sin(Ax)e^{Bx}\, dx = Ge^{Bx}\sin(Ax) - Je^{Bx}\cos(Ax) + C.$$

Exercises

1. Use the given formula to rewrite $\int \cos(3x)e^{4x}\, dx$.

2. Find the derivative of the expression you wrote in Exercise 1.

3. Use $\dfrac{d}{dx}\left[\int \cos(3x)e^{4x}\, dx\right] = \cos(3x)e^{4x}$ to find the values of D and F from Exercise 1.

   What is $\int \cos(3x)e^{4x}\, dx$?

4. Integrate $\int \cos(3x)e^{4x}\, dx$ using integration by parts. Compare the result to your answer from Exercise 3.

5. Rewrite the expression you wrote in Exercise 4 in terms of A, B, and x.

6. Integrate $\int \cos(Ax)e^{Bx}\, dx$ using integration by parts. Compare the result to your answer from Exercise 5.

7. Use the given formula to rewrite $\int \sin(5x)e^{2x}\, dx$.

8. Find the derivative of the expression you wrote in Exercise 7.

9. Use $\dfrac{d}{dx}\left[\int \sin(5x)e^{2x}\, dx\right] = \sin(5x)e^{2x}$ to find the values of G and J. What is $\int \sin(5x)e^{2x}\, dx$?

10. Integrate $\int \sin(5x)e^{2x}\, dx$ using integration by parts. Compare the result to your answer from Exercise 9.

11. Rewrite the expression you wrote in Exercise 10 in terms of A, B, and x.

12. Integrate $\int \sin(Ax)e^{Bx}\, dx$ using integration by parts. Compare the result to your answer from Exercise 11.

Chapter 9 Infinite Series

Chapter Comments

You may want to think of this chapter as two parts. Part I (Sections 9.1 through 9.6) covers sequences and series of constant terms and Part II (Sections 9.7 through 9.10) covers series with variable terms. Part I should be covered quickly so that most of your time in this chapter is spent on Part II.

In Sections 9.1 through 9.6, there are many different kinds of series and many different tests for convergence or divergence. Be sure to go over each of these carefully. It is a good idea to review the basic facts of each test each day before covering the new material for that day. This provides a review for students and also allows them to see the similarities and differences among tests. The table on page 636 in Section 9.6 is a good way to compare the various tests. Be sure to go over with your students the guidelines for choosing the appropriate test found on page 635.

The nth-Term Test for Divergence, Theorem 9.9 on page 603, is frequently misunderstood. Your students need to know that it proves divergence only and that it says nothing about convergence.

Sections 9.7 through 9.10 often seem difficult for students, so allow extra time for these sections. You will need to go over the material slowly and do many examples. Students should be able to find the coefficients of a Taylor or Maclaurin polynomial, write a Taylor series, derive a Taylor series from a basic list, and find the radius of convergence and the interval of convergence. Checking the endpoints should be a matter of recalling Sections 9.2 through 9.6.

Section 9.1 Sequences

Section Comments

9.1 **Sequences**—Write the terms of a sequence. Determine whether a sequence converges or diverges. Write a formula for the nth term of a sequence. Use properties of monotonic sequences and bounded sequences.

Teaching Tips

A good introduction to this section could be asking the following questions: Is there a sequence $\{a_n\}$ such that $\lim\limits_{x\to\infty} f(x)$ exists, but $\lim\limits_{n\to\infty} a_n$ does not? Could $\lim\limits_{n\to\infty} a_n$ exist, but not $\lim\limits_{x\to\infty} f(x)$?

Also, ask students if they can give an example of a sequence $\{a_n\}$ that is monotonic and bounded above and below, but $\lim\limits_{n\to\infty} a_n$ does not exist.

Point out to students that if $a_n = f(n)$ for some function $f(x)$ and if $\lim\limits_{x\to\infty} f(x) - L$, then $\lim\limits_{n\to\infty} a_n = L$. Thus, a_n converges if $f(x)$ has a horizontal asymptote as x approaches infinity. Be sure to stress to students that the converse is NOT true.

You may also want to show students an example using a recursive sequence such as $a_1 = 2$ and $a_{n+1} = 3a_n + 2$ for $n = 1, 2, 3, \ldots$.

Use the sample problem below to review the following concepts:

- Monotonic sequence

- Bounded sequence

- Unbounded sequence

- Theorem 9.5

Understanding these concepts is important for students so that they can successfully complete this chapter.

Give an example of a sequence satisfying the condition or explain why no such sequence exists. (Examples are not unique.)

(a) A monotonically increasing sequence that converges to 10

(b) A monotonically increasing bounded sequence that does not converge

(c) A sequence that converges to $\frac{3}{4}$

(d) An unbounded sequence that converges to 100

Review the definitions of the concepts listed above and then go over the solution. Note that examples are not unique, so students may write different sequences.

Solution

(a) $a_n = 10 - \dfrac{1}{n}$

(b) Impossible. The sequence converges by Theorem 9.5.

(c) $a_n = \dfrac{3n}{4n + 1}$

(d) Impossible. An unbounded sequence diverges.

How Do You See It? Exercise

Page 597, Exercise 72 The graphs of two sequences are shown in the figures. Which graph represents the sequence with alternating signs? Explain.

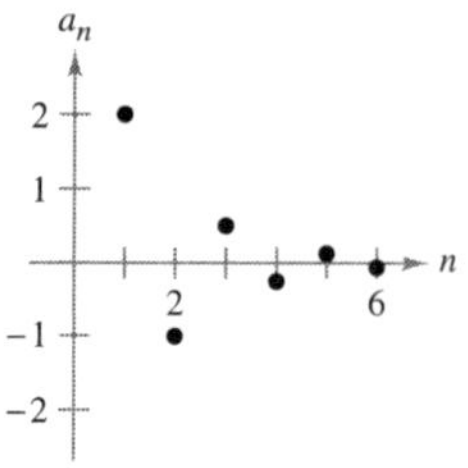

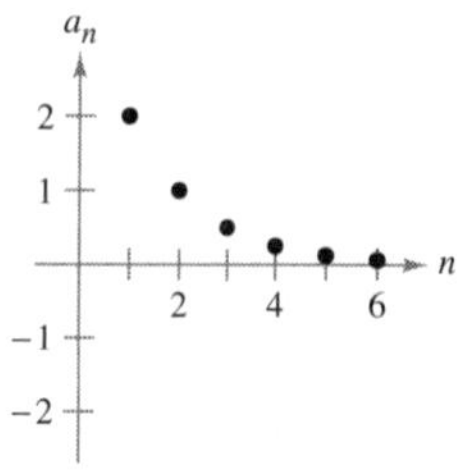

Solution

The graph on the left represents a sequence with alternating signs because the terms alternate from being above the x-axis to being below the x-axis.

Suggested Homework Assignment

Pages 596–598: 1–63 odd, 77, and 79.

Section 9.2 Series and Convergence

Section Comments

9.2   **Series and Convergence**—Understand the definition of a convergent infinite series. Use properties of infinite geometric series. Use the nth-Term Test for Divergence of an infinite series.

Teaching Tips

Begin the lesson by asking students if the following is always true, sometimes true, or always false: If the series $\sum_{n=1}^{\infty} a_n$ converges and the series $\sum_{n=1}^{\infty} b_n$ converges, then their sum converges. Lead students to the answer that this is always true. This will help students understand Theorem 9.7 in the text.

You may also wish to show students the following series and ask if it converges:

$0.2 + 0.02 + 0.002 + 0.0002 + \cdots$

During the lecture, derive for students the formula for the sum of a geometric series. Point out the reason why the series diverges when $|r| > 1$ and for $r = 1$ and $r = -1$.

You may want to represent a geometric series visually, such as $\sum_{n=1}^{\infty} \dfrac{1}{2^n} = 1$ shown below:

Give students a preview of the Integral Test by showing that $\sum_{n=1}^{\infty} \dfrac{1}{n}$ diverges by using an integral as a lower bound:

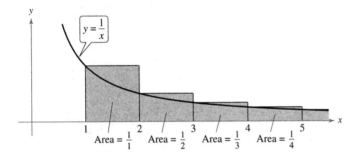

Use the sample problem below to review the following concepts:

- Theorem 9.8 and its converse

- Theorem 9.9

Are the following statements true? Why or why not?

(a) Because $\dfrac{1}{n^4}$ approaches 0 as n approaches infinity, $\sum_{n=1}^{\infty} \dfrac{1}{n^4} = 0$.

(b) Because $\lim_{n \to \infty} \dfrac{1}{\sqrt[4]{n}}$ the series $\sum_{n=1}^{\infty} \dfrac{1}{\sqrt[4]{n}}$ converges.

Go over Theorem 9.8 and note that its converse is not true (see the remark on page 603 near Theorem 9.8). In both parts, the given information (the expressions approach 0 as n approaches ∞) is irrelevant and Theorem 9.9 does not apply. So, neither statement is true.

Using a computer algebra system, you can find that $\sum_{n=1}^{\infty} \dfrac{1}{n^4} = \dfrac{\pi^4}{90}$ and that $\sum_{n=1}^{\infty} \dfrac{1}{\sqrt[4]{n}}$ diverges. Note that each series is a p-series, which will be covered in the next section (see Section 9.3).

Solution

(a) False. The fact that $\dfrac{1}{n^4} \to 0$ is irrelevant to the convergence of $\displaystyle\sum_{n=1}^{\infty} \dfrac{1}{n^4}$. Furthermore,

$$\sum_{n=1}^{\infty} \frac{1}{n^4} \neq 0.$$

(b) False. The fact that $\dfrac{1}{\sqrt[4]{n}} \to 0$ is irrelevant to the convergence of $\displaystyle\sum_{n=1}^{\infty} \dfrac{1}{\sqrt[4]{n}}$. In fact,

$$\sum_{n=1}^{\infty} \frac{1}{\sqrt[4]{n}} \text{ diverges.}$$

How Do You See It? Exercise

Page 608, Exercise 102 The figure below represents an informal way of showing that $\displaystyle\sum_{n=1}^{\infty} \dfrac{1}{n^2} < 2$. Explain how the figure implies this conclusion.

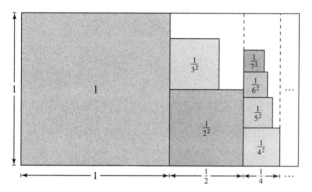

Solution

The entire rectangle has area 2 because the height is 1 and the base is $1 + \frac{1}{2} + \frac{1}{4} + \cdots = 2$. The squares all lie inside the rectangle, and the sum of their areas is

$$1 + \frac{1}{2^2} + \frac{1}{3^2} + \frac{1}{4^2} + \cdots.$$

So, $\displaystyle\sum_{n=1}^{\infty} \dfrac{1}{n^2} < 2$.

Suggested Homework Assignment

Pages 605–607: 1–65 odd and 91–97 odd.

Section 9.3 The Integral Test and *p*-Series

Section Comments

9.3   **The Integral Test and *p*-Series**—Use the Integral Test to determine whether an infinite series converges or diverges. Use properties of *p*-series and harmonic series.

Teaching Tips

Begin the lesson by stating the Integral Test and give a geometric justification.

Discuss the basic *p*-series $\displaystyle\sum_{n=1}^{\infty} \dfrac{1}{n^p}$, and determine the values of p for which it converges and diverges.

Use the sample problem below to review the following concepts:

- Theorem 9.10

- *p*-series

- Theorem 9.11

Use a graph to show that the inequality is true. What can you conclude about the convergence or divergence of the series? Explain.

(a) $\displaystyle\sum_{n=1}^{\infty} \frac{1}{\sqrt{n}} > \int_{1}^{\infty} \frac{1}{\sqrt{x}}\,dx$ \qquad (b) $\displaystyle\sum_{n=2}^{\infty} \frac{1}{n^2} < \int_{1}^{\infty} \frac{1}{x^2}\,dx$

Go over Theorem 9.10 and its proof. Then go over the solutions below. The solutions can be confirmed by noting that each series is a *p*-series and applying Theorem 9.11.

Solution

(a)

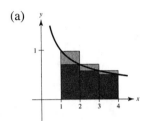

$$\sum_{n=1}^{\infty} \frac{1}{\sqrt{n}} > \int_{1}^{\infty} \frac{1}{\sqrt{x}}\,dx$$

The areas of the rectangles is greater than the area under the curve.

Because $\displaystyle\int_{1}^{\infty} \frac{1}{\sqrt{x}}\,dx = \left[2\sqrt{x}\right]_{1}^{\infty} = \infty$ diverges, $\displaystyle\sum_{n=1}^{\infty} \frac{1}{\sqrt{n}}$ diverges.

(b)

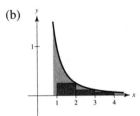

$$\sum_{n=2}^{\infty} \frac{1}{n^2} < \int_{1}^{\infty} \frac{1}{x^2}\,dx$$

The areas of the rectangle are less than the area under the curve.

Because $\displaystyle\int_{1}^{\infty} \frac{1}{x^2}\,dx = \left[-\frac{1}{x}\right]_{1}^{\infty} = 1$ converges, $\displaystyle\sum_{n=2}^{\infty} \frac{1}{n^2}$ converges $\left(\text{and so does } \displaystyle\sum_{n=1}^{\infty} \frac{1}{n^2}\right)$.

105

Page 614, Exercise 44 The graphs show the sequences of partial sums of the p-series

$$\sum_{n=1}^{\infty} \frac{1}{n^{0.4}} \quad \text{and} \quad \sum_{n=1}^{\infty} \frac{1}{n^{1.5}}.$$

Using Theorem 9.11, the first series diverges and the second series converges. Explain how the graphs show this.

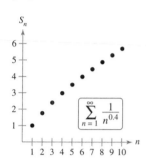
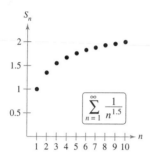

Solution

Answers will vary. *Sample answer:* The graph of the partial sums of the first series seems to be increasing without bound; therefore, the series diverges. The graph of the partial sums of the second series seems to be approaching a limit; therefore the series converges.

Suggested Homework Assignment

Pages 613–615: 1–37 odd, 53–63 odd, and 69–79 odd (for review).

Section 9.4 Comparisons of Series

Section Comments

9.4   **Comparisons of Series**—Use the Direct Comparison Test to determine whether a series converges or diverges. Use the Limit Comparison Test to determine whether a series converges or diverges.

Teaching Tips

Ask students when using the Limit Comparison Test why you need to check the conditions $a_n \leq b_n$ or $a_n \geq b_n$ only for $n \geq N$, where N is an integer. Lead students to the answer that for any integer N, the sum of the first N terms of the series is finite.

You may also wish to ask: If the improper integral $\displaystyle\int_3^{\infty} \frac{dx}{x^p}$ converges, which series *must* converge?

$$\sum_{n=1}^{\infty} \frac{1}{n^{p+1}}, \quad \sum_{n=3}^{\infty} \frac{1}{n^{p+1}}, \quad \sum_{n=1}^{\infty} \frac{1}{n^{p-1}}, \quad \text{or} \quad \sum_{n=3}^{\infty} \frac{1}{n^{p-1}}$$

Use Exercise 48 on page 621 to review the following concepts:

- Comparison of series

- p-series

- Harmonic series

The main point here is that the tests in this section compare *series*, not just a few terms. Also, you can review *p*-series and harmonic series.

Solution

This is not correct. The beginning terms do not affect the convergence or divergence of a series. In fact,

$$\frac{1}{1000} + \frac{1}{1001} + \cdots = \sum_{n=1000}^{\infty} \frac{1}{n} \text{ diverges (harmonic) and}$$

$$1 + \frac{1}{4} + \frac{1}{9} + \cdots = \sum_{n=1}^{\infty} \frac{1}{n^2} \text{ converges (}p\text{-series).}$$

How Do You See It? Exercise

Page 621, Exercise 52 The figure shows the first 20 terms of the series $\Sigma\, c_n$ using squares and the first 20 terms of the series $\Sigma\, d_n$ using circles. If $\Sigma\, d_n$ converges, can you determine anything about the convergence or divergence of $\Sigma\, c_n$? Explain.

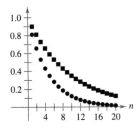

Solution

You cannot conclude anything. If you knew instead that $\Sigma\, c_n$ converges, then you could write that $\Sigma\, d_n$ converges by direct comparison.

Suggested Homework Assignment

Pages 620–622: 1, 5–33 odd, 37–45 odd, and 53–57 odd.

Section 9.5 Alternating Series

Section Comments

9.5   **Alternating Series**—Use the Alternating Series Test to determine whether an infinite series converges. Use the Alternating Series Remainder to approximate the sum of an alternating series. Classify a convergent series as absolutely or conditionally convergent. Rearrange an infinite series to obtain a different sum.

Teaching Tips

Ask students to consider $f(x) = \dfrac{x^2}{x^3 + 1}$ and $f'(x) = \dfrac{x(2 - x^3)}{(x^3 + 1)^2}$ to help determine if the series $\displaystyle\sum_{n=1}^{\infty} (-1)^{n+1} \dfrac{n^2}{n^3 + 1}$ converges. Lead students to the answer that when examining f', you can show that f is a decreasing function and you can use the Alternating Series Test to show it converges.

You may also want to ask if $\displaystyle\sum_{n=1}^{\infty} \sin\left(\dfrac{\pi n}{2}\right) x^{-1/2}$ converges or diverges and why.

For $\displaystyle\sum_{n=1}^{\infty} \dfrac{(-1)^{n+1}}{n}$, show students that the associated absolute value series of $\displaystyle\sum_{n=1}^{\infty} \dfrac{1}{n}$ diverges and that for $\displaystyle\sum_{n=0}^{\infty} (1.1)^{-n} \cos n\pi = \displaystyle\sum_{n=0}^{\infty} (-1)^n (1.1)^{-n}$, the associated series $\displaystyle\sum_{n=0}^{\infty} (1.1)^{-n}$ converges.

Another good example to point out to the class is to write out the first five partial sums of $\displaystyle\sum_{n=1}^{\infty} \dfrac{1}{n}$, $\displaystyle\sum_{n=1}^{\infty} -\dfrac{1}{n}$, and $\displaystyle\sum_{n=1}^{\infty} \dfrac{(-1)^{n+1}}{n}$ and graph the solutions. Ask students to describe the patterns.

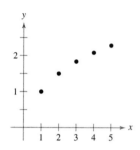 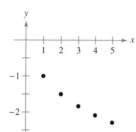 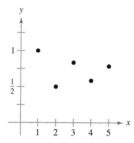

Use Exercise 61 on page 630 to review the following concepts:

- Theorem 9.16

- Absolute convergence

- Conditional convergence

Review the above concepts and then go over the solution. In part (a), ask students to classify a_n as absolutely or conditionally convergent.

Solution

(a) False. For example, let $a_n = \dfrac{(-1)^n}{n}$. Then $\displaystyle\sum a_n = \displaystyle\sum \dfrac{(-1)^n}{n}$ converges and

$\displaystyle\sum (-a_n) = \displaystyle\sum \dfrac{(-1)^{n+1}}{n}$ converges. But, $\displaystyle\sum |a_n| = \displaystyle\sum \dfrac{1}{n}$ diverges.

(b) True. If $\displaystyle\sum |a_n|$ converged, then so would $\displaystyle\sum a_n$ by Theorem 9.16.

How Do You See It? Exercise

Page 630, Exercise 62 The graphs of the sequences of partial sums of two series are shown in the figures. Which graph represents the partial sums of an alternating series? Explain.

(a)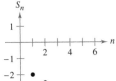

(b)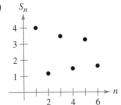

Solution

(b). The partial sums alternate above and below the horizontal line representing the sum.

Suggested Homework Assignment

Pages 629–630: 1, 3, 9–27 odd, 31, 37, 41–55 odd, and 71–79 odd (for review).

Section 9.6 The Ratio and Root Tests

Section Comments

9.6   **The Ratio and Root Tests**—Use the Ratio Test to determine whether a series converges or diverges. Use the Root Test to determine whether a series converges or diverges. Review the tests for convergence and divergence of an infinite series.

Teaching Tips

Begin the lesson by asking students if the following are true or false:

(a) If a series is absolutely convergent, then it is convergent.

(b) If a series is convergent, then it is absolutely convergent.

You may also want to ask students what can be said about the convergence of

$$\sum_{n=1}^{\infty} a_n \text{ if } \lim_{n\to\infty} \left| \frac{a_{n+1}}{a_n} \right| = 1.$$

Be sure to work out Examples 2–5 in the text and to point out the Summary of Tests for Series on page 636.

Use the following exercise to review the following concepts:

- Ratio Test

- Root Test

What can you conclude about the convergence or divergence of $\sum a_n$ for each of the following conditions? Explain your reasoning.

(a) $\lim\limits_{n\to\infty} \left| \dfrac{a_{n+1}}{a_n} \right| = 0$ (b) $\lim\limits_{n\to\infty} \left| \dfrac{a_{n+1}}{a_n} \right| = 1$ (c) $\lim\limits_{n\to\infty} \left| \dfrac{a_{n+1}}{a_n} \right| = \dfrac{3}{2}$

(d) $\lim\limits_{n\to\infty} \sqrt[n]{|a_n|} = 2$ (e) $\lim\limits_{n\to\infty} \sqrt[n]{|a_n|} = 1$ (f) $\lim\limits_{n\to\infty} \sqrt[n]{|a_n|} = e$

Review the Ratio and Root Tests (Theorems 9.17 and 9.18, respectively). Then apply the Ratio Test to parts (a)–(c) and the Root Test to parts (d)–(f).

109

Solution

(a) Converges   (Ratio Test)

(b) Inconclusive   (See Ratio Test.)

(c) Diverges   (Ratio Test)

(d) Diverges   (Root Test)

(e) Inconclusive   (See Root Test.)

(f) Diverges   (Root Test, $e > 1$)

How Do You See It? Exercise

Page 639, Exercise 96 The graphs show the sequence of partial sums of the series

$$\sum_{n=1}^{\infty} \frac{2^n}{n} \quad \text{and} \quad \sum_{n=1}^{\infty} \frac{n}{3^n}.$$

Using the Ratio Test, the first series diverges and the second series converges. Explain how the graphs show this.

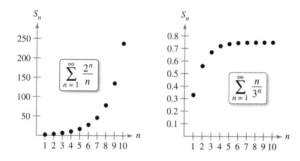

Solution

The first graph shows the sequence of partial sums increasing without bound. So, the first series diverges. The second graph shows the sequence of partial sums approaching 0.75. So, the second series converges.

Suggested Homework Assignment

Pages 637–638: 1–5 odd, 17–51 odd, 53–69 odd (for review), and 71.

Section 9.7 Taylor Polynomials and Approximations

Section Comments

9.7   **Taylor Polynomials and Approximations**—Find polynomial approximations of elementary functions and compare them with the elementary functions. Find Taylor and Maclaurin polynomial approximations of elementary functions. Use the remainder of a Taylor polynomial.

Teaching Tips

Use Exercise 36 to review the following concepts:

- Taylor polynomials

- Natural exponential function

110

Go over the definition of *n*th Taylor polynomial. You can also review the natural exponential function and its derivative. The conclusions in part (c) are also discussed in Example 2 and the *Technology* note on page 641.

Solution

(a) $f(x) = e^x$ $\qquad\qquad\qquad$ $f(1) = e$

$\quad$ $f'(x) = e^x$ $\qquad\qquad\qquad$ $f'(1) = e$

$\quad$ $f''(x) = f'''(x) = f^{(4)}(x) = e^x$ and $f''(1) = f'''(1) = f^{(4)}(1) = e$

$\quad$ $P_1(x) = e + e(x - 1)$

$\quad$ $P_2(x) = e + e(x - 1) + \dfrac{e}{2}(x - 1)^2$

$\quad$ $P_4(x) = e + e(x - 1) + \dfrac{e}{2}(x - 1)^2 + \dfrac{e}{6}(x - 1)^3 + \dfrac{e}{24}(x - 1)^4$

x	1.00	1.25	1.50	1.75	2.00
e^x	e	3.4093	4.4817	5.7546	7.3891
$P_1(x)$	e	3.3979	4.0774	4.7570	5.4366
$P_2(x)$	e	3.4828	4.4172	5.5215	6.7957
$P_4(x)$	e	3.4903	4.4809	5.7485	7.3620

(b)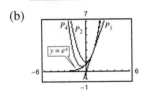

(c) As the degree increases, the accuracy increases. As the distance from x to 1 increases, the accuracy decreases.

How Do You See It? Exercise

Page 650, Exercise 66 The figure shows the graphs of the first-, second-, and third-degree polynomial approximations P_1, P_2, and P_3 of a function f. Label the graphs of P_1, P_2, and P_3. To print an enlarged copy of the graph, go to *MathGraphs.com*.

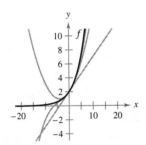

Solution

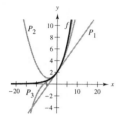

Suggested Homework Assignment

Pages 648–650: 1, 3, 11, 13, 17, 21, 23, 27–31 odd, 39, 45, 51–55 odd, and 61.

Section 9.8 Power Series

Section Comments

9.8   **Power Series**—Understand the definition of a power series. Find the radius and interval of convergence of a power series. Determine the endpoint convergence of a power series. Differentiate and integrate a power series.

Teaching Tips

Begin class by asking students if the interval of convergence of a power series has a length of 2, what is the radius of convergence? Lead students to the answer that the radius is 1.

Also, ask students that if a power series $\sum\limits_{n=1}^{\infty} a_n x^n$ has a radius of convergence of 3, what do you know about $\sum\limits_{n=1}^{\infty} a_n 3^n$, $\sum\limits_{n=1}^{\infty} a_n(-2)^n$, and $\sum\limits_{n=1}^{\infty} a_n 5^n$? Lead students to the answer that you know nothing about the first series without further investigation. The second converges and the third diverges.

Be sure to give the definition of power series, noting that the value of the series depends on x. Make sure to point out to students how power series differ from numerical series.

Talk about the role of partial sums of power series and how these polynomials approximate the series for values of x near a.

Use the following exercise to review the following concepts:

* Power series

* Radius and interval of convergence

Write a power series that has the indicated interval of convergence. Explain your reasoning.

(a) $(-2, 2)$ (b) $(-1, 1]$

(c) $(-1, 0)$ (d) $[-2, 6)$

Review the above terms and then go over the solution. Be sure that your students understand that there are many possible answers.

Solution

Many answers are possible.

(a) $\displaystyle\sum_{n=1}^{\infty} \left(\frac{x}{2}\right)^n$

Geometric: $\left|\dfrac{x}{2}\right| < 1 \implies |x| < 2$

(b) $\displaystyle\sum_{n=1}^{\infty} \frac{(-1)^n x^n}{n}$ converges for $-1 < x \leq 1$.

(c) $\displaystyle\sum_{n=1}^{\infty} (2x + 1)^n$

Geometric: $|2x + 1| < 1 \implies -1 < x < 0$

(d) $\displaystyle\sum_{n=1}^{\infty} \frac{(x - 2)^n}{n4^n}$ converges for $-2 \leq x < 6$.

How Do You See It? Exercise

Page 659, Exercise 56 Match the graph of the first 10 terms of the sequence of partial sums of the series

$$g(x) = \sum_{n=0}^{\infty} \left(\frac{x}{3}\right)^n$$

with the indicated value of the function. [The graphs are labeled (i), (ii), (iii), and (iv).] Explain how you made your choice.

(i)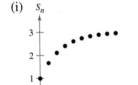

(ii)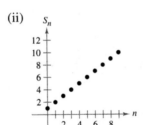

(iii)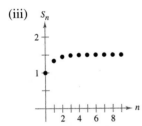

(iv)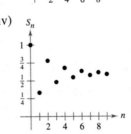

(a) $g(1)$ (b) $g(2)$ (c) $g(3)$ (d) $g(-2)$

Solution

(a) $g(1) = \sum_{n=0}^{\infty} \left(\frac{1}{3}\right)^n = 1 + \frac{1}{3} + \frac{1}{9} + \cdots$

$S_1 = 1, S_2 = \frac{4}{3}, \ldots$

Matches (iii).

(b) $g(2) = \sum_{n=0}^{\infty} \left(\frac{2}{3}\right)^n = 1 + \frac{2}{3} + \frac{4}{9} + \cdots$

$S_1 = 1, S_2 = \frac{5}{3}, \ldots$

Matches (i).

(c) $g(3) = \sum_{n=0}^{\infty} \left(\frac{3}{3}\right)^n = 1 + 1 + 1 + \cdots$

$S_1 = 1, S_2 = 2, \ldots$

Matches (ii).

(d) $g(-2) = \sum_{n=0}^{\infty} \left(\frac{-2}{3}\right)^n = 1 - \frac{2}{3} + \frac{4}{9} - \cdots$ (alternating)

$S_1 = 1, S_2 = \frac{1}{3}, S_3 = \frac{7}{9}, \ldots$

Matches (iv).

Suggested Homework Assignment

Pages 658–659: 1, 3, 5, 11, 15–35 odd, and 49.

Section 9.9 Representation of Functions by Power Series

Section Comments

9.9   **Representation of Functions by Power Series**—Find a geometric power series that represents a function. Construct a power series using series operations.

Teaching Tips

Begin the lesson by asking students about changing indices for series. For example, ask students what the difference is between $\sum_{n=1}^{\infty} nx^{n-1}$ and $\sum_{n=0}^{\infty} (n+1)x^n$. Students need to see that $n+1$ is substituted for n. So, you are starting the series at $n = 0$ instead of $n = 1$. Stress to the class that students must be careful of the indices.

Use the following exercise to review the following concepts:

- Operations with power series

- Interval of convergence

Describe why the statement is incorrect.

$$\sum_{n=0}^{\infty} x^n + \sum_{n=0}^{\infty} \left(\frac{x}{5}\right)^n = \sum_{n=0}^{\infty} \left(1 + \frac{1}{5}\right)x^n \qquad \times$$

Review the Operations with Power Series on page 663 and go over the solution. You can also use this exercise to review interval of convergence. Ask students to determine the interval of convergence for each series, $\sum_{n=0}^{\infty} x^n$ and $\sum_{n=0}^{\infty} \left(\frac{x}{5}\right)^n$. The intervals of convergence are $(-1, 1)$ and and $(-5, 5)$, respectively. What is the interval of convergence for the sum $\sum_{n=0}^{\infty} x^n + \sum_{n=0}^{\infty} \left(\frac{x}{5}\right)^n$?

The answer is the intersection of the intervals of convergence of the two original series, $(-1, 1)$.

Solution

You can verify that the statement is incorrect by calculating the constant terms of each side:

$$\sum_{n=0}^{\infty} x^n + \sum_{n=0}^{\infty} \left(\frac{x}{5}\right)^n = (1 + 1) + \left(x + \frac{x}{5}\right) + \cdots$$

$$\sum_{n=0}^{\infty} \left(1 + \frac{1}{5}\right) x^n = \left(1 + \frac{1}{5}\right) + \left(1 + \frac{1}{5}\right) x + \cdots$$

The formula should be $\sum_{n=0}^{\infty} x^n + \sum_{n=0}^{\infty} \left(\frac{x}{5}\right)^n = \sum_{n=0}^{\infty} \left[1 + \left(\frac{1}{5}\right)^n\right] x^n$.

How Do You See It? Exercise

Page 667, Exercise 56 The figure on the left shows the graph of a function. The figure on the right shows the graph of a power series representation of the function.

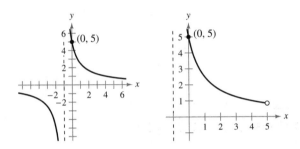

(a) Identify the function.

(b) What are the center and interval of convergence of the power series?

Solution

(a) The function is $f(x) = \dfrac{5}{1 + x}$.

(b) Expanding f at $c = 2$ gives

$$f(x) = \frac{5}{1 + x} = \frac{5}{3 + (x - 2)} = \frac{5/3}{1 - \left(\dfrac{2 - x}{3}\right)}.$$

The geometric series for this function converges on

$$\left|\frac{2 - x}{3}\right| < 1 \implies |2 - x| < 3 \implies (-1, 5).$$

Suggested Homework Assignment

Pages 666–667: 1, 3, 7, 15, 23, 25, 33, 35, and 37.

Section 9.10 Taylor and Maclaurin Series

Section Comments

9.10   **Taylor and Maclaurin Series**—Find a Taylor or Maclaurin series for a function. Find a binomial series. Use a basic list of Taylor series to find other Taylor series.

Teaching Tips

Ask students which of the following statements are true and which are false:

(a) A Taylor series is a special type of Maclaurin series.

(b) A Maclaurin series is a special type of Taylor series.

Use the sample problem below to review the following concepts:

- Power series

- Natural exponential function

Explain how to use the series $g(x) = e^x = \sum\limits_{n=0}^{\infty} \dfrac{x^n}{n!}$ to find the series for each function. Do not find the series.

(a) $f(x) = e^{-x}$

(b) $f(x) = e^{3x}$

(c) $f(x) = xe^x$

(d) $f(x) = e^{2x} + e^{-2x}$

Review the power series for the natural exponential function. Then go over the solution.

Solution

(a) Replace x with $(-x)$.

(b) Replace x with $3x$.

(c) Multiply series by x.

(d) Replace x with $2x$, then replace x with $-2x$, and add the two together.

How Do You See It? Exercise

Page 678, Exercise 78 Identify the function represented by each power series and match the function with its graph. [The graphs are labeled (i) and (ii).]

(i)
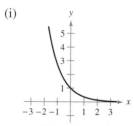

(ii)
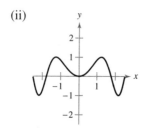

(a) $\sum\limits_{n=0}^{\infty} \dfrac{(-1)^n x^{4n+2}}{(2n+1)!}$ (b) $\sum\limits_{n=0}^{\infty} \dfrac{(-1)^n x^n}{n!}$

Solution

(a) This is the series for $f(x) = \sin x^2$. Matches (ii).

(b) This is the series for $f(x) = e^{-x}$. Matches (i).

Suggested Homework Assignment

Pages 677–678: 1, 3, 7–13 odd, 17, 23, 27, 31, 49, and 63–69 odd.

Chapter 9 Project

Chasing a Pot of Gold

You are standing at the beginning of a sidewalk, 1000 meters from a pot of gold. You walk toward the pot of gold at a rate of 1 meter per second. After each second, the sidewalk stretches uniformly and instantaneously, increasing its length by 1000 meters.

Exercises

1. What is the total length of the sidewalk after 1 second?

2. How far are you from the pot of gold after 1 second?

3. What is the total length of the sidewalk after 2 seconds?

4. How far are you from the pot of gold after 2 seconds?

In Exercises 5–11, consider the sequence $\{d_n\}$ where d_n is your distance from the pot of gold after n seconds but before the road stretches.

5. Find d_0, d_1, d_2, d_3, and d_4.

6. Find an expression for d_1 in terms of d_0. Similarly, find an expression for d_2, d_3, and d_4 in terms of d_1, d_2, and d_3, respectively.

7. Use the expressions you wrote in Exercise 6 to show that $d_1 = 1(d_0 - 1)$,
$$d_2 = 2\left(d_0 - \left(1 + \tfrac{1}{2}\right)\right), \text{ and } d_3 = 3\left[d_0 - \left(1 + \tfrac{1}{2} + \tfrac{1}{3}\right)\right].$$

8. Use the results from Exercise 7 to write an expression for d_n in terms of d_0.

9. Does the series $\displaystyle\sum_{k=1}^{\infty} \frac{1}{k}$ converge or diverge? What theorem did you use?

10. What does your answer to Exercise 9 imply about the value of d_n for large values of n? What does this mean in the context of the problem?

11. Use the integral $\displaystyle\int_{1}^{n+1} \frac{1}{x}\, dx$ to approximate how long it will take to reach the pot of gold.

In Exercises 12 and 13, suppose the sidewalk is still 1000 meters long, but you walk toward the pot of gold at a speed of 0.25 meter per second.

12. Write an expression for d_n in terms of d_0.

13. Will you reach the pot of gold? If so, approximately how long will it take?

In Exercises 14 and 15, suppose the sidewalk is 5000 meters long, you walk toward the pot of gold at a speed of 1 meter per second, and the sidewalk stretches 5000 meters after every second.

14. Write an expression for d_n in terms of d_0.

15. Will you reach the pot of gold? If so, approximately how long will it take?

16. Does the length of the sidewalk or the speed at which you walk impact whether you reach the pot of gold? Explain.

Chapter 10 Conics, Parametric Equations, and Polar Coordinates

Chapter Comments

For each of the conics (parabola, circle, ellipse, and hyperbola), your students should be able to write the equation in standard form; identify the center, radius, vertices, foci, directrix, axes, or asymptotes; and sketch the graph using these facts. Many of these concepts will be used when quadric surfaces are discussed in Section 11.6. A review of the circle can be found in Appendix C.

Eccentricity for ellipses is discussed on page 691 and for hyperbolas on page 694. For a discussion of rotation of axes and the use of the discriminant to determine which conic the general second-degree equation represents, see Appendix D.

Be sure to do some of the real-life applications in Section 10.1, such as the length of a parabolic cable used for a bridge (Exercise 65 on page 698).

When you discuss parametric equations in Section 10.2, be sure to point out to your students that a parametric representation for a curve is not unique. Therefore, their answers may be correct, yet they may not agree with those provided in the back of the book. The process of writing parametric equations for a given rectangular equation should convince your students of this. The opposite process, eliminating the parameter, sometimes involves adjusting the domain, as in Example 2 of Section 10.2. When graphing in parametric form, have your students note the orientation. For example, $x = 2 \cos \theta$ and $y = 2 \sin \theta$ graphs a circle counterclockwise, but $x = 2 \sin \theta$ and $y = 2 \cos \theta$ graphs the same circle clockwise.

Parametric form of the derivative is discussed in Section 10.3. Be sure to point out to students that the slope of the tangent line is $\dfrac{dy}{dx}$ and not $\dfrac{dy}{dt}$. Students very often have difficulty with the higher-order derivatives with respect to x. For example, to find $\dfrac{d^2y}{dx^2}$, they forget to divide $\dfrac{d}{dt}\left(\dfrac{dy}{dx}\right)$ by $\dfrac{dx}{dt}$. Arc length for parametric equations of a curve is a concept that will be expanded in 3-space (Section 12.5).

Polar coordinates, discussed in Section 10.4, use only radian measure for the angle θ. Point out to your students that when plotting points in polar coordinates, it is usually easier to find the angle first and then mark off r units on the terminal side of the angle. Note, too, that contrary to rectangular coordinates, a point can be represented many ways in polar coordinates. Students should know the equations for coordinate conversion found in Theorem 10.10 on page 720.

Curve sketching in polar coordinates can be time consuming and tedious. Don't get bogged down in this. Your students should easily recognize limaçons and rose curves from the equation and be able to sketch them quickly. Use a graphing utility and note the orientation.

Area, discussed in Section 10.5, is an important idea for a good understanding of polar coordinates. The difficulty here is in finding the limits of integration. Note that there may be points of intersection of two curves given in polar coordinates that do not show up from solving simultaneously. Therefore, it is necessary to graph the curves.

Section 10.6 on conics in polar form may be omitted if time is a problem in your course.

Section 10.1 Conics and Calculus

Section Comments

10.1   Conics and Calculus—Understand the definition of a conic section. Analyze and write equations of parabolas using properties of parabolas. Analyze and write equations of ellipses using properties of ellipses. Analyze and write equations of hyperbolas using properties of hyperbolas.

Teaching Tips

For an introduction to conics, you may want to show a video of how the conics arise from the intersection of a plane and a double-napped cone: *http://www.youtube.com/watch?v=GDHNoQHQmtQ*

You may also wish to bring in two traffic cones to demonstrate the double-napped cone.

To show how an ellipse is formed, have one piece of string tied to two thumbtacks and move a pen or piece of chalk around the string keeping it taut.

We suggest Exercise 57 to review the following concepts:

- Circle

- Parabola

- Ellipse

- Hyperbola

A review of the circle can be found in Appendix C. A discussion of the use of the discriminant to determine which conic the general second-degree equation represents can be found in Appendix D.

Go over the solution below. You can extend the exercise by asking students to identify the center, radius, vertices, foci, directrix, axes, or asymptotes, and sketch the graph using these facts.

In part (d), you could also eliminate the x^2-term.

Solution

$9x^2 + 4y^2 - 36x - 24y - 36 = 0$

(a) $9(x^2 - 4x + 4) + 4(y^2 - 6y + 9) = 36 + 36 + 36$

$$9(x - 2)^2 + 4(y - 3)^2 = 108$$

$$\frac{(x - 2)^2}{12} + \frac{(y - 3)^2}{27} = 1$$

   Ellipse

(b) $9x^2 - 4y^2 - 36x - 24y - 36 = 0$

$9(x^2 - 4x + 4) - 4(y^2 + 6y + 9) = 36 + 36 - 36$

$$\frac{(x - 2)^2}{4} - \frac{(y - 3)^2}{9} = 1$$

   Hyperbola

(c) $4x^2 + 4y^2 - 36x - 24y - 36 = 0$

$$4\left(x^2 - 9x + \frac{81}{4}\right) + 4(y^2 - 6y + 9) = 36 + 81 + 36$$

$$\left(x - \frac{9}{2}\right)^2 + (y - 3)^2 = \frac{153}{4}$$

Circle

(d) *Sample answer:* Eliminate the y^2-term.

How Do You See It? Exercise

Page 697, Exercise 60 Describe in words how a plane could intersect with the double-napped cone to form each conic section (see figure).

(a) Circle   (b) Ellipse

(c) Parabola   (d) Hyperbola

Solution

(a) A circle is formed when a plane intersects the top or bottom half of a double-napped cone and is perpendicular to the axis of the cone.

(b) An ellipse is formed when a plane intersects only the top or bottom half of a double-napped cone but is not parallel or perpendicular to the axis of the cone, is not parallel to the side of the cone, and does not intersect the vertex.

(c) A parabola is formed when a plane intersects the top or bottom half of a double-napped cone, is parallel to the side of the cone, and does not intersect the vertex.

(d) A hyperbola is formed when a plane intersects both halves of a double-napped cone, is parallel to the axis of the cone, and does not intersect the vertex.

Suggested Homework Assignment

Pages 696–697: 1–9 odd, 15, 17, 29, 33, 39, 43, and 51–55 odd.

Section 10.2 Plane Curves and Parametric Equations

Section Comments

10.2   Plane Curves and Parametric Equations—Sketch the graph of a curve given by a set of parametric equations. Eliminate the parameter in a set of parametric equations. Find a set of parametric equations to represent a curve. Understand two classic calculus problems, the tautochrone and brachistochrone problems.

121

Teaching Tips

Begin the lesson by asking students what the difference is between a function and a parametric curve. Lead students to the answer that the graph of a function can be made into a parametric curve, but not necessarily the other way around. A function has to pass the Vertical Line Test and a parametric curve does not.

You may want to sketch the parametric curve $x(t) = \sin t$, $y(t) = t^2$, for $0 \le t \le \pi$ and ask the students if $(1\ \pi/4)$ is on the curve.

Other important points to stress to the students are:

1. Discuss the process of going from a parametric curve to a relation between x and y.

2. Describe the difference between the graph of a function and a parametric curve. Caution students to take appropriate care in sketching parametric curves, especially concerning questions of range and direction.

3. Show how reversing the functions $x(t)$ and $y(t)$ yields the inverse of a given relation.

Use the sample problem below to review the following concepts:

- Parametric equations

- Eliminating the parameter

- Transformation of a graph

- Orientation of a curve

Consider the parametric equations $x = 8 \cos t$ and $y = 8 \sin t$.

(a) Describe the curve represented by the parametric equations.

(b) How does the curve represented by the parametric equations $x = 8 \cos t + 3$ and $y = 8 \sin t + 6$ compare to the curve described in part (a)?

(c) How does the original curve change when cosine and sine are interchanged?

In part (a), eliminate the parameter t to obtain a rectangular equation of the circle. Sketch a graph and note the orientation. The parametric equations in part (b) represent a horizontal shift 3 units right and a vertical shift 6 units upward of the circle described in part (a). In part (c), the parametric equations are $x = 8 \sin t$ and $y = 8 \cos t$. You may need to sketch the graphs or use a table of values (see below) to convince students that the orientation is reversed. They can also see the orientation by using a graphing utility in *parametric mode* to graph the circles.

t	0	$\dfrac{\pi}{4}$	$\dfrac{\pi}{2}$	$\dfrac{3\pi}{4}$	π
$x = 8 \cos t$	8	$4\sqrt{2}$	0	$-4\sqrt{2}$	-8
$x = 8 \sin t$	0	$4\sqrt{2}$	8	$4\sqrt{2}$	0

t	0	$\dfrac{\pi}{4}$	$\dfrac{\pi}{2}$	$\dfrac{3\pi}{4}$	π
$x = 8 \sin t$	0	$4\sqrt{2}$	8	$4\sqrt{2}$	0
$x = 8 \cos t$	8	$4\sqrt{2}$	0	$-4\sqrt{2}$	-8

122

In general, the graph of the parametric equations

$x = h + r \cos \theta$ and $y = h + r \sin \theta$, $0 \le \theta \le 2\pi$

is the circle (traced counterclockwise) given by

$(x - h)^2 + (y - k)^2 = r^2$.

In general, the graph of the parametric equations

$x = h + r \sin \theta$ and $y = h + \cos \theta$, $0 \le \theta \le 2\pi$

is the circle (traced clockwise) given by

$(x - h)^2 + (y - k)^2 = r^2$.

Solution

$x = 8 \cos t, \ y = 8 \sin t$

(a) $\left(\dfrac{x}{8}\right)^2 + \left(\dfrac{y}{8}\right)^2 = \cos^2 t + \sin^2 t = 1$

$x^2 + y^2 = 64$, Circle of radius 8

Center: $(0, 0)$ Oriented counterclockwise

(b) Circle of radius 8, but center: $(3, 6)$

(c) The orientation is reversed.

How Do You See It? Exercise

Page 708, Exercise 70 Which set of parametric equations is shown in the graph below? Explain your reasoning.

(a) $x = t$ (b) $x = t^2$

   $y = t^2$ $y = t$

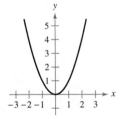

Solution

The graph matches (a) because $x = t \implies y = t^2 = x^2$. For (b), you have $y = t \implies x = t^2 = y^2$, which is not the correct parabola.

Suggested Homework Assignment

Pages 707–708: 1, 3, 5, 13, 17, 25, 43, 47, 53, 55, and 61.

Section 10.3 Parametric Equations and Calculus

Section Comments

10.3 **Parametric Equations and Calculus**—Find the slope of a tangent line to a curve given by a set of parametric equations. Find the arc length of a curve given by a set of parametric equations. Find the area of a surface of revolution (parametric form).

Teaching Tips

Begin class by asking students why the parametric curve $x = f(t)$, $y = g(t)$ has a horizontal tangent line when $dy/dt = 0$ and dx/dt does not equal zero, and not the other way around. Lead students to the answer that dy/dt gives the rate of change in the vertical direction.

Make sure the formula for the area enclosed by a parametric curve is developed.

Ask students to observe that the parabola $y = x^2$ is concave upward, and the parabola $y = -x^2$ is concave downward. Ask students to see if they think that the parabola given by $x(t) = t^2$, $y(t) = t$ is concave upward or concave downward. Use the second derivatives to answer these questions. $d^2x/dx^2 = -1/t$ shows that the bottom part is concave upward and the top part is concave downward.

Ask students to consider the following parametric curve: $x(t) = \sin(t)$, $y(t) = \cos t$. Find the equation of the tangent line when $t = \pi/2$. Find the points where the tangent line is vertical and horizontal.

You may want to give students a preview of polar coordinates at this point by having them find the area of the ellipse $x^2 + y^2 = 1$ using the parameterization $x = \cos t$ and $y = \sin t$.

Present an arc length problem using $x = t^2 + 1$, $y = t^2 - 1$ on $[0, 2]$.

Use the sample problem below to review the following concepts:

- Graphs of parametric equations

- Derivatives of parametric equations

(a) Sketch a graph of a curve defined by the parametric equations $x = g(t)$, $y = f(t)$ such that $dx/dt > 0$ and $dy/dt < 0$ for all real numbers t.

(b) Sketch a graph of a curve defined by the parametric equations $x = g(t)$, $y = f(t)$ such that $dx/dt < 0$ and $dy/dt < 0$ for all real numbers t.

There are many possible answers. Sample answers are given below. Note in part (a) that $dx/dt = 1 > 0$ and $dy/dt = -1 < 0$. In part (b), $dx/dt = -1 < 0$ and $dy/dt = -1 < 0$.

Solution

(a) One possible answer is the graph given by $x = t$, $y = -t$.

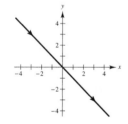

(b) One possible answer is the graph given by $x = -t$, $y = -t$.

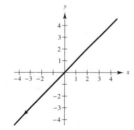

124

How Do You See It? Exercise

Page 717, Exercise 76 Using the graph of f, (a) determine whether dy/dt is positive or negative given that dx/dt is negative and (b) determine whether dx/dt is positive or negative given that dy/dt is positive. Explain your reasoning.

(i)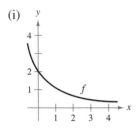

(ii)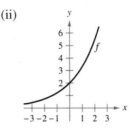

Solution

(i) (a) $\dfrac{dx}{dt} < 0$ and $\dfrac{dy}{dx} < 0$ from the graph. So, $\dfrac{dy}{dt} > 0$ because $\dfrac{dy}{dx} = \dfrac{dy/dt}{dx/dt}$.

   (b) $\dfrac{dy}{dt} > 0$ and $\dfrac{dy}{dx} < 0$ from the graph. So, $\dfrac{dx}{dt} < 0$ because $\dfrac{dy}{dx} = \dfrac{dy/dt}{dx/dt}$.

(ii) (a) $\dfrac{dx}{dt} < 0$ and $\dfrac{dy}{dx} > 0$ from the graph. So, $\dfrac{dy}{dt} < 0$ because $\dfrac{dy}{dx} = \dfrac{dy/dt}{dx/dt}$.

   (b) $\dfrac{dy}{dt} > 0$ and $\dfrac{dy}{dx} > 0$ from the graph. So, $\dfrac{dx}{dt} > 0$ because $\dfrac{dy}{dx} = \dfrac{dy/dt}{dx/dt}$.

Suggested Homework Assignment

Pages 715–716: 1–5 odd, 11, 15, 19, 29, 35, 43, and 51.

Section 10.4 Polar Coordinates and Polar Graphs

Section Comments

10.4   Polar Coordinates and Polar Graphs—Understand the polar coordinate system. Rewrite rectangular coordinates and equations in polar form and vice versa. Sketch the graph of an equation given in polar form. Find the slope of a tangent line to a polar graph. Identify several types of special polar graphs.

Teaching Tips

You may want to begin with an intuitive definition of polar coordinates and derive the algebraic formulas, with special attention given to the fact that the graph of a polar function need not pass the Vertical Line Test. Sketch a polar curve such as $r = \sin\theta$ or $r = 1 - \sin\theta$ by plotting several points and connecting the points.

Derive the formula for the slope of a polar curve $r = f(\theta)$ by viewing this equation as a parametric function $x(\theta) = f(\theta)\cos\theta$, $y(\theta) = f(\theta)\sin\theta$. Discuss the horizontal tangent lines and the vertical tangent lines.

Use the sample problem below to review the following concepts:

- Polar coordinates

- Theorem 10.10

- Polar-to-rectangular conversion

- Identifying the graph of a polar equation

125

Describe the graphs of the following polar equations.

(a) $r = 7$ (b) $r^2 = 7$

(c) $r = \dfrac{7}{\cos \theta}$ (d) $r = \dfrac{7}{\sin \theta}$

(e) $r = 7 \cos \theta$ (f) $r = 7 \sin \theta$

Review the definition of polar coordinates and Theorem 10.10 (see pages 719 and 720). Then go over the solution below. Have students confirm these results by using a graphing utility in *polar mode* to graph the equations.

Solution

(a) $r = 7$: Circle with radius 7 and centered at origin

(b) $r^2 = 7$: Circle with radius $\sqrt{7}$ and centered at origin

(c) $r = \dfrac{7}{\cos \theta} \implies r \cos \theta = x = 7$: Vertical line through the point $(7, 0)$

(d) $r = \dfrac{7}{\sin \theta} \implies r \sin \theta = y = 7$: Horizontal line through the point $(0, 7)$

(e) $r = 7 \cos \theta$: Circle with radius $\dfrac{7}{2}$ and centered at $\left(\dfrac{7}{2}, 0 \right)$

(f) $r = 7 \sin \theta$: Circle with radius $\dfrac{7}{2}$ and centered at $\left(0, \dfrac{7}{2} \right)$

How Do You See It? Exercise

Page 726, Exercise 56 Identify each special polar graph and write its equation.

(a)

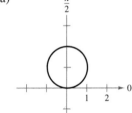

(b)

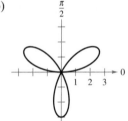

(c)

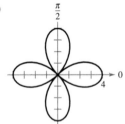

(d)

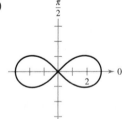

Solution

(a) The graph is a circle, where $a = 2$ is measured along the y-axis. So, the equation of the polar graph is $r = 2 \sin \theta$.

(b) The graph is a rose curve with $n = 3$ petals and $a = 3$. So, the equation of the polar graph is $r = 3 \sin 3\theta$.

126

(c) The graph is a rose curve with $2n = 4$ petals and $a = 4$. So, the equation of the polar graph is $r = 4 \cos 2\theta$.

(d) The graph is a lemniscate with $a = 3$, which is measured along the x-axis. So, the equation of the polar graph is $r^2 = 9 \cos 2\theta$.

Suggested Homework Assignment

Pages 726–727: 1, 3, 7, 17, 31, 37, 45, 51, and 73–91 odd.

Section 10.5 Area and Arc Length in Polar Coordinates

Section Comments

10.5   **Area and Arc Length in Polar Coordinates**—Find the area of a region bounded by a polar graph. Find the points of intersection of two polar graphs. Find the arc length of a polar graph. Find the area of a surface of revolution (polar form).

Teaching Tips

Derive the general formula for area in polar coordinates, $A = \dfrac{1}{2}\displaystyle\int_{\alpha}^{\beta} f(\theta)^2 \, d\theta$.

Find the area inside $r = 2 \cos \theta$ but outside $r = 1$.

Find the integral for the length of the three-leaved rose curve $r = \cos 3\theta$ by first finding the length from $\theta = 0$ to $\theta = \pi/6$.

Inform students that $r = \theta$ is a spiral and find the area for $[0, 2\pi]$.

Use Exercises 71 and 72 to review the following concepts:

- Sketching the graph of a polar equation

- Finding the area of a region bounded by a polar graph using a geometric formula

- Finding the area of a region bounded by a polar graph using Theorem 10.13

Sketch the graph and determine the interval that traces the graph only once. In both cases, the interval is $0 \le \theta < \pi$. You may need to demonstrate this using a table of values or showing how the graph is traced out on a graphing utility in *polar mode*. The geometric formula for the area of a circle is $A = \pi r^2$. Because the radius in Exercise 71 is 5, the area is 25π. Because the radius in Exercise 72 is $5/2$, the area is $25\pi/4$. To use integration to find the area, apply Theorem 10.13 as follows.

71. $A = 2\left(\dfrac{1}{2}\right)\displaystyle\int_{0}^{\pi/2} [10 \cos \theta]^2 \, d\theta$

$\quad = 100 \displaystyle\int_{0}^{\pi/2} \cos^2 \theta \, d\theta$

$\quad = 50 \displaystyle\int_{0}^{\pi/2} (1 + \cos 2\theta) \, d\theta$

$\quad = 50\left[\theta + \dfrac{\sin 2\theta}{2} \right]_{0}^{\pi/2}$

$\quad = 25\pi$

72. $A = 2\left(\dfrac{1}{2}\right)\displaystyle\int_{0}^{\pi/2} [5 \sin \theta]^2 \, d\theta$

$\quad = 25 \displaystyle\int_{0}^{\pi/2} \sin^2 \theta \, d\theta$

$\quad = \dfrac{25}{2} \displaystyle\int_{0}^{\pi/2} (1 - \cos 2\theta) \, d\theta$

$\quad = \dfrac{25}{2}\left[\theta - \dfrac{\sin 2\theta}{2} \right]_{0}^{\pi/2}$

$\quad = \dfrac{25\pi}{4}$

Solution

71. $r = 10 \cos \theta, \ 0 \leq \theta < \pi$ **72.** $r = 5 \sin \theta, \ 0 \leq \theta < \pi$

     Circle of radius 5   Circle of radius $\frac{5}{2}$

     Area $= 25\pi$ Area $= \frac{25}{4}\pi$

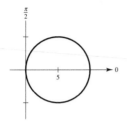 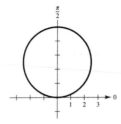

How Do You See It? Exercise

Page 737, Exercise 74 Which graph, traced out only once, has a larger arc length? Explain your reasoning.

(a) 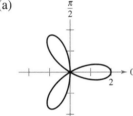   (b)

Solution

Graph (b) has a larger arc length because it has more leaves.

Suggested Homework Assignment

Pages 735–736: 1, 5, 9, 13, 21, 29, 37, 57, and 59.

Section 10.6 Polar Equations of Conics and Kepler's Laws

Section Comments

10.6   **Polar Equations of Conics and Kepler's Laws**—Analyze and write polar equations of conics. Understand and use Kepler's Laws of planetary motion.

Teaching Tips

Use the sample problem below to review the following concepts:

- Parabolas

- Polar equations of parabolas

- Theorems 10.16 and 10.17

Explain how the graph of each conic differs from the graph of $r = \dfrac{4}{1 + \sin \theta}$.

(a) $r = \dfrac{4}{1 - \cos\theta}$ (b) $r = \dfrac{4}{1 - \sin\theta}$

(c) $r = \dfrac{4}{1 + \cos\theta}$ (d) $r = \dfrac{4}{1 - \sin(\theta - \pi/4)}$

Go over Theorems 10.16 and 10.17, and then the solution given below. Have students confirm these results by using a graphing utility in *polar mode* to graph the equations.

Solution

$r = \dfrac{4}{1 + \sin\theta}$ is a parabola with horizontal directrix above the pole.

(a) Parabola with vertical directrix to left of pole

(b) Parabola with horizontal directrix below pole

(c) Parabola with vertical directrix to right of pole

(d) Parabola (b) rotated counterclockwise $\dfrac{\pi}{4}$

How Do You See It? Exercise

Page 744, Exercise 48 Identify the conic in the graph and give the possible values for the eccentricity.

(a)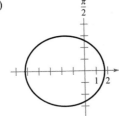

(b)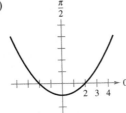

(c)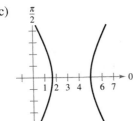

(d)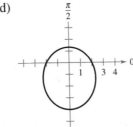

Solution

(a) The conic is an ellipse, so $0 < e < 1$.

(b) The conic is a parabola, so $e = 1$.

(c) The conic is a hyperbola, so $e > 1$.

(d) The conic is an ellipse, so $0 < e < 1$.

Suggested Homework Assignment

Pages 743–744: 1, 7–11 odd, 15, 23, 29, 35, and 43.

Chapter 10 Project

Path of a Baseball

A baseball is hit 3 feet above home plate at a 45° angle with the horizontal. Its initial speed is 100 feet per second. The path of the baseball at any time t (in seconds) is given by the parametric equations

$$x = 100(\cos 45°)t \quad \text{and} \quad y = 3 + 100(\sin 45°)t - 16t^2.$$

Exercises

1. Find $\dfrac{dy}{dx}$.

2. At what time is the ball at its maximum height?

3. What is the maximum height of the ball?

4. When the ball is at its maximum height, what is its vertical velocity?

5. When the ball is at its maximum height, what is its horizontal velocity?

6. How long is the ball in the air?

7. How far is the ball from home plate when it hits the ground?

8. Find the value of $\dfrac{dy}{dx}$ at the instant the ball hits the ground. What does this mean in the context of the problem?

9. What is the vertical velocity of the ball at impact?

10. What is the horizontal velocity of the ball at impact?

11. A 14-foot fence is located 300 feet from home plate. Will the ball clear the fence? Explain.

12. Set up a definite integral to determine the total length of the path traveled by the ball.

13. Use a graphing utility to evaluate the integral you wrote in Exercise 12. Compare this to your answer from Exercise 7.

14. Find a rectangular equation for the position of the ball by eliminating the parameter t.

15. Find the derivative of the function you wrote in Exercise 14.

16. According to the rectangular equation, for what value of x is the ball at its maximum height?

17. Use your answer from Exercise 16 and the equation $x = 100(\cos 45°)t$ to find when the ball is at its maximum height. Compare this to your answer from Exercise 2.

18. Why is it beneficial to express the path of the baseball with parametric equations rather than a rectangular equation? Explain.

Chapter 11   Vectors and the Geometry of Space

Chapter Comments

All of the ideas in this chapter need to be discussed in order for your students to have a good understanding of vectors. Point out to your students that vectors are not little pointed arrows, but that a directed line segment is just our way of representing a vector geometrically. Also note that this geometric representation of a vector does not have location. It does have direction and magnitude. On page 772 in the text is a Remark about the words *perpendicular, orthogonal,* and *normal.* This is worth discussing with your students because sometimes it seems that these words are used interchangeably.

The dot product of two vectors is sometimes referred to as scalar multiplication and the cross product as vector multiplication. The reason for this is because the dot product is a *scalar* and the cross product is a *vector.* Point out this distinction to your students. The way to find a cross product is to use a 3-by-3 determinant. You will probably have to show your students how to calculate this.

When discussing lines and planes in space, Section 11.5, point out to your students that direction numbers are not unique. If a, b, c is a set of direction numbers for a line or a plane, then ka, kb, kc, where $k \in R$, $k \neq 0$, is also a set of direction numbers for that line or plane.

The distance formulas in Section 11.5 between a point and a plane and between a point and a line need not be memorized. However, go over these so that students know where they are when they need to look them up.

It is important for your students to be familiar with the surfaces in space discussed in Section 11.6. The concepts in Chapters 14 and 15 will be much easier if students immediately recognize from the given equation which of the six surfaces on pages 800 and 801 is under discussion.

Two alternate coordinate systems are discussed in Section 11.7. The cylindrical coordinate system should be familiar to your students because it is an extension of the polar coordinate system in the plane. However, the spherical coordinate system will probably be new to students. Time spent here understanding this system will be rewarded in Chapters 14 and 15 when you are performing multiple integrations.

Section 11.1 Vectors in the Plane

Section Comments

11.1   **Vectors in the Plane**—Write the component form of a vector. Perform vector operations and interpret the results geometrically. Write a vector as a linear combination of standard unit vectors.

Teaching Tips

Often, students get confused by the definition of parallel vectors. As an aid, ask students if the vectors shown in the figure below are parallel.

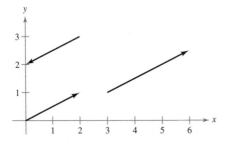

Ask students if $\mathbf{a} = \langle a_1, a_2, a_3 \rangle$, where $a_2 > 0$ and $a_3 < 0$, is the z-component of $-4\mathbf{a}$ positive or negative?

Please be sure to point out to students that the position representation for $\mathbf{a} = a_1\mathbf{i} + a_2\mathbf{j} + a_3\mathbf{k}$ has an endpoint of $P(a_1, a_2, a_3)$. Make sure to show why $\mathbf{i} + \mathbf{j}$ is NOT a unit vector but $\mathbf{i}$ and $\mathbf{j}$ are.

Make sure to present geometric representations of the parallelogram law and make sure students understand that a line is determined by a point and a vector, and a plane by a point and two vectors.

You may also wish to find unit vectors in the directions of $\langle 4, 0, 0 \rangle$, $\langle 2, 2, 0 \rangle$, and $\langle 3, 4, 5 \rangle$ and talk about what is happening geometrically.

Use the sample problem below to review the following concepts:

- Writing the component form of a vector

- Writing a vector as a linear combination of standard unit vectors

- Sketching a vector

- Finding the magnitude of a vector

The initial and terminal points of vector $\mathbf{v}$ are $(3, -4)$ and $(9, 1)$, respectively.

(a) Write $\mathbf{v}$ in component form.

(b) Write $\mathbf{v}$ as the linear combination of the standard unit vectors $\mathbf{i}$ and $\mathbf{j}$.

(c) Sketch $\mathbf{v}$ with its initial point at the origin.

(d) Find the magnitude of $\mathbf{v}$.

Go over the above concepts and the solution below.

Solution

(a) $\mathbf{v} = \langle 9 - 3, 1 - (-4) \rangle = \langle 6, 5 \rangle$

(b) $\mathbf{v} = 6\mathbf{i} + 5\mathbf{j}$

(c)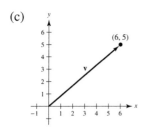

(d) $\|\mathbf{v}\| = \sqrt{6^2 + 5^2} = \sqrt{61}$

How Do You See It? Exercise

Page 760, Exercise 60 Use the figure to determine whether each statement is true or false. Justify your answer.

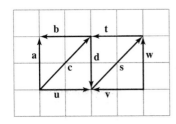

(a) $\mathbf{a} = -\mathbf{d}$ (b) $\mathbf{c} = \mathbf{s}$

(c) $\mathbf{a} + \mathbf{u} = \mathbf{c}$ (d) $\mathbf{v} + \mathbf{w} = -\mathbf{s}$

(e) $\mathbf{a} + \mathbf{d} = \mathbf{0}$ (f) $\mathbf{u} - \mathbf{v} = -2(\mathbf{b} + \mathbf{t})$

Solution

(a) True. $\mathbf{d}$ has the same magnitude as $\mathbf{a}$ but is in the opposite direction.

(b) True. $\mathbf{c}$ and $\mathbf{s}$ have the same length and direction.

(c) True. $\mathbf{a}$ and $\mathbf{u}$ are the adjacent sides of a parallelogram. So, the resultant vector, $\mathbf{a} + \mathbf{u}$, is the diagonal of the parallelogram, $\mathbf{c}$.

(d) False. The negative of a vector has the opposite direction of the original vector.

(e) True. $\mathbf{a} + \mathbf{d} = \mathbf{a} + (-\mathbf{a}) = \mathbf{0}$

(f) False. $\mathbf{u} - \mathbf{v} = \mathbf{u} - (-\mathbf{u}) = 2\mathbf{u}$

$$-2(\mathbf{b} + \mathbf{t}) = -2(\mathbf{b} + \mathbf{b}) = -2(2\mathbf{b}) = -2[2(-\mathbf{u})] = -4\mathbf{u}$$

Suggested Homework Assignment

Pages 759–761: 1, 5, 11, 21, 25, 35, 41, 47, 65, 71, 79, and 85–93 odd.

Section 11.2 Space Coordinates and Vectors in Space

Section Comments

11.2   Space Coordinates and Vectors in Space—Understand the three-dimensional rectangular coordinate system. Analyze vectors in space.

Teaching Tips

Begin this lesson by asking students what they think the equation $y = x$ is in three-dimensional space.

In helping students understand three-dimensional space, treat the blackboard as the yz-plane, the left wall as the xz-plane, and the floor as the xy-plane.

You could mark off one corner of the classroom with tape and determine coordinates of various things in the classroom using (x, y, z) coordinates.

Show students the equation of a circular cylinder in R^3 using the equation $x^2 + y^2 = r^2$. You can then go on to describe cylindrical surfaces as $y = 2x^2$ or $x^2 - y^2 = 9$.

You may want to show students what the triangular surface $x + y + z = 1$, where $x, y, z \geq 0$, looks like. This will be an important example for students to know when multiple integration is discussed.

Use Exercise 95 to review the following concepts:

- Recognizing a geometric figure generated by the terminal points of three vectors

- Vector addition

- Scalar multiplication

The figure given in the solution is a sample figure. However, the end result— that the terminal points of the vectors are collinear—is the same. As you go over the solution, you can review vector operations such as addition and scalar multiplication.

Solution

The terminal points of the vectors $t\mathbf{v}$, $\mathbf{u} + t\mathbf{v}$, and $s\mathbf{u} + t\mathbf{v}$ are collinear.

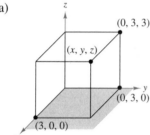

How Do You See It? Exercise

Page 769, Exercise 94 Determine (x, y, z) for each figure. Then find the component form of the vector from the point on the x-axis to the point (x, y, z).

(a)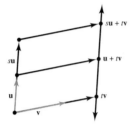

(b)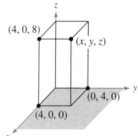

Solution

(a) $(x, y, z^2) = (3, 3, 3)$

$\mathbf{v} = \langle 3, 3, 3 \rangle - \langle 3, 0, 0 \rangle$

$= \langle 3 - 3, 3 - 0, 3 - 0 \rangle = \langle 0, 3, 3 \rangle$

(b) $(x, y, z) = (4, 4, 8)$

$\mathbf{v} = \langle 4, 4, 8 \rangle - \langle 4, 0, 0 \rangle$

$= \langle 4 - 4, 4 - 0, 8 - 0 \rangle = \langle 0, 4, 8 \rangle$

Suggested Homework Assignment

Pages 767–769: 1, 3, 7, 11, 13–25 odd, 33, 39, 45, 51, 55, 57, 61, 63, 67, 71, 75, 79, 85, and 101.

134

Section 11.3 The Dot Product of Two Vectors

Section Comments

11.3 **The Dot Product of Two Vectors**—Use properties of the dot product of two vectors. Find the angle between two vectors using the dot product. Find the direction cosines of a vector in space. Find the projection of a vector onto another vector. Use vectors to find the work done by a constant force.

Teaching Tips

Inform students that the answers to dot products will always result in a scalar. This will be an important difference between dot products and cross products.

Be sure to do application problems such as Examples 7 and 8. You may want to also show the students Exercise 57 and 59.

How Do You See It? Exercise

Page 777, Exercise 48 What is known about θ, the angle between two nonzero vectors $\mathbf{u}$ and $\mathbf{v}$, when

(a) $\mathbf{u} \cdot \mathbf{v} = 0$?   (b) $\mathbf{u} \cdot \mathbf{v} > 0$?   (c) $\mathbf{u} \cdot \mathbf{v} < 0$?

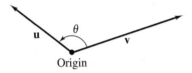

Solution

(a) Orthogonal, $\theta = \dfrac{\pi}{2}$ (b) Acute, $0 < \theta < \dfrac{\pi}{2}$ (c) Obtuse, $\dfrac{\pi}{2} < \theta < \pi$

Suggested Homework Assignment

Pages 777–778: 1, 7, 13, 17, 25, 29, 31, 37, 43, 57, and 59.

Section 11.4 The Cross Product of Two Vectors in Space

Section Comments

11.4 **The Cross Product of Two Vectors in Space**—Find the cross product of two vectors in space. Use the triple scalar product of three vectors in space.

Teaching Tips

Point out to the class that the process to find cross products is the exact same process for finding a determinant of a 3 × 3 matrix. Point out the two methods using a matrix

$$\begin{bmatrix} 1 & 2 & 3 \\ 3 & -5 & 7 \\ -1 & 6 & 4 \end{bmatrix}$$

and then the cross product of $\mathbf{u} \times \mathbf{v}$ in general. The result will be another vector and NOT a scalar, as with the dot product.

You may want to explain the geometry involved for finding the volume of a parallelepiped.

How Do You See It? Exercise

Page 786, Exercise 42 The vertices of a triangle in space are (x_1, y_1, z_1), (x_2, y_2, z_2), and (x_3, y_3, z_3). Explain how to find a vector perpendicular to the triangle.

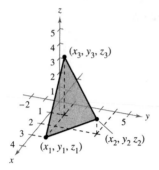

Solution

Form the vectors for two sides of the triangle, and compute their cross product.

$$\langle x_2 - x_1, y_2 - y_1, z_2 - z_1 \rangle \times \langle x_2 - x_1, y_2 - y_1, z_2 - z_1 \rangle$$

Suggested Homework Assignment

Pages 785–786: 1, 7, 11, 17, 23, 25, 35, 37, 43, and 45.

Section 11.5 Lines and Planes in Space

Section Comments

11.5 **Lines and Planes in Space**—Write a set of parametric equations for a line in space. Write a linear equation to represent a plane in space. Sketch the plane given by a linear equation. Find the distances between points, planes, and lines in space.

Teaching Tips

When specifying the equation of a line in space, the text mentions that you need a point on the line and a vector parallel to the line. Ask students why you can't determine a line in space by only using one vector. Lead students to the important answer that one vector would give the direction of the line, but it could be placed anywhere in space.

Stress to students that there are three ways to describe a line:

1. Vector or parametric equations starting with initial point P_i on the line and in direction **v**

2. By symmetric equations: $\dfrac{x - x_1}{a} = \dfrac{y - y_1}{b} = \dfrac{z - z_1}{c}$

3. Two-point vector equation starting with P_i and Q_i on the line

In addition, inform students that there are three ways to describe a plane:

1. Vector equation starting with P_i and normal vector **n**

2. Scalar equation: $ax + by + cz + d = 0$

3. Parametric equations starting with P_i and two direction vectors **u** and **v**

Stress to students *that a line is determined by a point and a direction, and a plane is determined by a point and a normal vector or a point and two direction vectors.*

136

Use the sample problem below to review the following concepts:

- Parametric equations of a line (Theorem 11.11)

- Symmetric equations of a line

- Standard equation of a plane in space (Theorem 11.12)

- General form of an equation of a plane in space

Go over the definitions of each concept listed above (see pages 787 and 788). Then note which equation or set of equations matches the correct choice.

Match the equation or set of equations with the description it represents.

(a) Set of parametric equations of a line

(b) Set of symmetric equations of a line

(c) Standard equation of a plane in space

(d) General form of an equation of a plane in space

(i) $\dfrac{x-6}{2} = \dfrac{y+1}{-3} = \dfrac{z}{1}$

(ii) $2x - 7y + 5z + 10 = 0$

(iii) $x = 4 + 7t,\ y = 3 + t,\ z = 3 - 3t$

(iv) $2(x - 1) + (y + 3) - 4(z - 5) = 0$

Solution

(a) Matches (iii).

(b) Matches (i).

(c) Matches (iv).

(d) Matches (ii).

How Do You See It? Exercise

Page 796, Exercise 104 Match the general equation with its graph. Then state what axis or plane the equation is parallel to.

(a) $ax + by + d = 0$ (b) $ax + d = 0$

(c) $cz + d = 0$ (d) $ax + cz + d = 0$

(i)

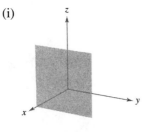

(ii)

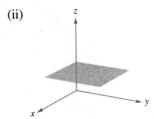

(iii)

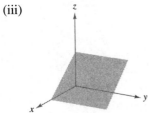

(iv)

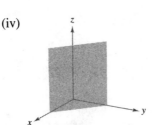

Solution

(a) $ax + by + d = 0$ matches (iv). The plane is parallel to the z-axis.

(b) $ax + d = 0$ matches (i). The plane is parallel to the yz-plane.

(c) $cz + d = 0$ matches (ii). The plane is parallel to the xy-plane.

(d) $ax + cz + d = 0$ matches (iii). The plane is parallel to the y-axis.

Suggested Homework Assignment

Pages 794–797: 1, 3, 11, 15, 17–23 odd, 27, 31, 35, 37, 41, 45–55 odd, 59, 63, 65, 75–81 odd, 89, 93, 97, 99, 109, and 111.

Section 11.6 Surfaces in Space

Section Comments

11.6   Surfaces in Space—Recognize and write equations of cylindrical surfaces. Recognize and write equations of quadric surfaces. Recognize and write equations of surfaces of revolution.

Teaching Tips

Begin this lesson by asking students what the axis is of the circular cylinder $x^2 + z^2 = 1$.

You may also want to ask students to think about what the vertical traces are of the surface $z = x^2 + y^2$, the horizontal traces for $z > 0$, and the horizontal traces for $z < 0$.

If you have access to a computer algebra system, demonstrate how the program can be used to graph these surfaces.

Use the following exercise to review the following concepts:

- Recognizing the generating curve for a cylinder

- Recognizing equations for cylindrical surfaces

What does the equation $z = x^2$ represent in the xz-plane? What does it represent in three-space?

Go over the definition of a cylinder and equations of cylinders on page 798. Then go over the solution. A graph of the cylinder is shown below and is provided on a transparency. The generating curve is a parabola in the xz-plane. The rulings of the cylinder are parallel to the y-axis.

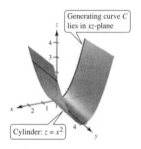

Solution

In the xz-plane, $z = x^2$ is a parabola. In three-space, $z = x^2$ is a cylinder.

138

How Do You See It? Exercise

Page 806, Exercise 30 The four figures below are graphs of the quadric surface $z = x^2 + y^2$. Match each of the four graphs with the point in space from which the paraboloid is viewed.

(a)

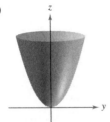

(b)

(c)

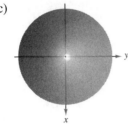

(d)

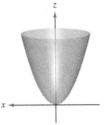

(i) $(0, 0, 20)$

(ii) $(0, 20, 0)$

(iii) $(20, 0, 0)$

(iv) $(10, 10, 20)$

Solution

$z = x^2 + y^2$

(a) You are viewing the paraboloid from the x-axis: $(20, 0, 0)$

(b) You are viewing the paraboloid from above, but not on the z-axis: $(10, 10, 20)$

(c) You are viewing the paraboloid from the z-axis: $(0, 0, 20)$

(d) You are viewing the paraboloid from the y-axis: $(0, 20, 0)$

Suggested Homework Assignment

Pages 806–807: 1, 3, 5–9 odd, 11, 15–25 odd, 31–35 odd, and 39.

Section 11.7 Cylindrical and Spherical Coordinates

Section Comments

11.7   Cylindrical and Spherical Coordinates—Use cylindrical coordinates to represent surfaces in space. Use spherical coordinates to represent surfaces in space.

Teaching Tips

We suggest the sample problem below to review the following concepts:

- Cylindrical coordinates and surfaces in space

- Spherical coordinates and surfaces in space

(a) For constants a, b, and c, describe the graphs of the equations $r = a$, $\theta = b$, and $z = c$ in cylindrical coordinates.

139

(b) For constants a, b, and c, describe the graphs of the equations $\rho = a$, $\theta = b$, and $\phi = c$ in spherical coordinates.

Go over the cylindrical coordinate system (see page 808). As you go over part (a), refer to Figures 11.69 and 11.70. Then go over the spherical coordinate system (see page 811). As you go over part (b), refer to Figure 11.76.

Solution

(a) $r = a$ Cylinder with z-axis symmetry

    $\theta = b$ Plane perpendicular to xy-plane

    $z = c$ Plane parallel to xy-plane

(b) $\rho = a$ Sphere

    $\theta = b$ Vertical half-plane

    $\phi = c$ Half-cone

How Do You See It? Exercise

Page 814, Exercise 78 Identify the surface graphed and match the graph with its rectangular equation. Then find an equation in cylindrical coordinates for the equation given in rectangular coordinates.

(a) 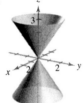   (b)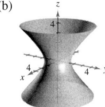

(i) $x^2 + y^2 = \frac{4}{9}z^2$ (ii) $x^2 + y^2 - z^2 = 2$

Solution

(a) The surface is a cone. The equation is (i)

$$x^2 + y^2 = \frac{4}{9}z^2.$$

In cylindrical coordinates, the equation is

$$x^2 + y^2 = \frac{4}{9}z^2$$
$$r^2 = \frac{4}{9}z^2$$
$$r = \frac{2}{3}z.$$

(b) The surface is a hyperboloid of one sheet. The equation is (ii) $x^2 + y^2 - z^2 = 2$. In cylindrical coordinates, the equation is

$$x^2 + y^2 - z^2 = 2$$
$$r^2 - z^2 = 2$$
$$r^2 = z^2 + 2.$$

Chapter 11 Project

Bond Angles

The study of the properties of molecules involves determining a molecule's three-dimensional, geometrical arrangement or molecular structure. Molecular structure is described in terms of bond distances and bond angles. A bond distance is defined as the distance of the straight line connecting the nuclei of two bonded atoms. A bond angle is the angle between any two bonded distances that include a common atom.

Exercises

Use the figure at the right as a representation of a methane molecule, CH_4. The hydrogen atoms are located at $(0, 0, 0)$, $(1, 1, 0)$, $(1, 0, 1)$, and $(0, 1, 1)$, and the carbon atom is located at $\left(\frac{1}{2}, \frac{1}{2}, \frac{1}{2}\right)$.

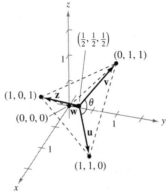

1. Find the component form of **u**.

2. Find $\|\mathbf{u}\|$.

3. Find the component form of **v**.

4. Find $\|\mathbf{v}\|$.

5. Find $\mathbf{u} \cdot \mathbf{v}$.

6. Use your answers from Exercises 1–5 to determine the bond angle between the hydrogen atoms located at $(1, 1, 0)$ and $(0, 1, 1)$.

7. Determine the bond distance between the hydrogen atoms located at $(1, 1, 0)$ and $(0, 1, 1)$.

8. Find $\|\mathbf{w}\|$ and $\|\mathbf{z}\|$.

In Exercises 9–13, determine the bond angle and the distance between the hydrogen atoms located at the given points.

9. $(0, 0, 0)$ and $(1, 1, 0)$

10. $(1, 0, 1)$ and $(1, 1, 0)$

11. $(0, 1, 1)$ and $(0, 0, 0)$

12. $(0, 1, 1)$ and $(1, 0, 1)$

13. $(0, 0, 0)$ and $(1, 0, 1)$

14. Classify the triangles formed by connecting the nuclei of two hydrogen atoms and the carbon atom of a methane molecule. Explain.

Chapter 12 Vector-Valued Functions

Chapter Comments

In discussing vector-valued functions with your students, be sure to distinguish them from real-valued functions. A vector-valued function is a vector, whereas a real-valued function is a real number. Remind your students that the parameterization of a curve is not unique. As discussed on page 822 at the end of Example 3, the choice of a parameter determines the orientation of the curve.

Sections 12.1 and 12.2 of this chapter discuss the domain, limit, continuity, differentiation, and integration of vector-valued functions. Go over these concepts carefully because they are the basis for the applications discussed in Sections 12.3, 12.4, and 12.5. Be sure to point out that when integrating a vector-valued function, the constant of integration is a vector, not a real number.

Go over all of the ideas presented in Sections 12.3, 12.4, and 12.5. Some, such as arc length, will be familiar to your students. Choose your assignments carefully in these sections as the problems are lengthy. Be sure to assign problems with a mix of functions, transcendental as well as algebraic.

If you are pressed for time, it is not necessary to cover every formula for curvature. However, do not omit this idea entirely.

Section 12.1 Vector-Valued Functions

Section Comments

12.1   **Vector-Valued Functions**—Analyze and sketch a space curve given by a vector-valued function. Extend the concepts of limits and continuity to vector-valued functions.

Teaching Tips

Be sure to clearly explain the differences and similarities between vector functions and parametric equations for a planar curve.

Describe the differences between the parameterizations $\langle \sin t, \cos t \rangle$ and $\langle \sin t^2, \cos t^2 \rangle$ graphically in terms of the domain of the parameter needed for one full revolution $[0, 2\pi]$.

Use Exercise 80 to review the following concepts:

- Vector-valued functions

- Analyzing a space curve given by a vector-valued function

Go over the definition of a vector-valued function on page 820. Then write the parametric equations and the rectangular equations as shown in the solution. Note that the curve represented by each vector-valued function is an ellipse.

Solution

(a) $x = -3 \cos t + 1,\ y = 5 \sin t + 2,\ z = 4$

$$\frac{(x-1)^2}{9} + \frac{(y-2)^2}{25} = 1,\ z = 4$$

(b) $x = 4,\ y = -3 \cos t + 1,\ z = 5 \sin t + 2$

$$\frac{(y-1)^2}{9} + \frac{(z-2)^2}{25} = 1,\ x = 4$$

(c) $x = 3 \cos t - 1, y = -5 \sin t - 2, z = 4$

$$\frac{(x+1)^2}{9} + \frac{(y+2)^2}{25} = 1, z = 4$$

(d) $x = -3 \cos 2t + 1, y = 5 \sin 2t + 2, z = 4$

$$\frac{(x-1)^2}{9} + \frac{(y-2)^2}{25} = 1, z = 4$$

(a) and (d) represent the same graph.

How Do You See It? Exercise

Page 827, Exercise 82 The four figures below are graphs of the vector-valued function $\mathbf{r}(t) = 4 \cos t\mathbf{i} + 4 \sin t\mathbf{j} + (t/4)\mathbf{k}$. Match each of the four graphs with the point in space from which the helix is viewed.

(a)

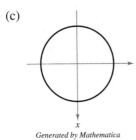

Generated by Mathematica

(b)

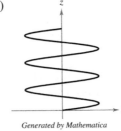

Generated by Mathematica

(c)

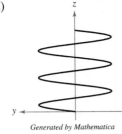

Generated by Mathematica

(d)

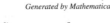
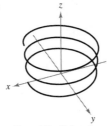

Generated by Mathematica

(i) $(0, 0, 20)$ (ii) $(20, 0, 0)$

(iii) $(-20, 0, 0)$ (iv) $(10, 20, 10)$

Solution

(a) View from the negative x-axis: $(-20, 0, 0)$

(b) View from above the first octant: $(10, 20, 10)$

(c) View from the z-axis: $(0, 0, 20)$

(d) View from the positive x-axis: $(20, 0, 0)$

Suggested Homework Assignment

Pages 825–826: 1, 3, 7, 15, 19, 21, 23, 27, 31, 35, 47–53 odd, 65–75 odd.

Section 12.2 Differentiation and Integration of Vector-Valued Functions

Section Comments

12.2   **Differentiation and Integration of Vector-Valued Functions**—Differentiate a vector-valued function. Integrate a vector-valued function.

Teaching Tips

Begin the lesson by asking students what they think the difference is between the tangent vector to a curve at a point P and the unit tangent vector to a curve at a point P. Lead students to the answer that the tangent vector can have any length, while the unit tangent vector has length 1.

Use the sample problem below to review the following concepts:

- Sketching a curve represented by a vector-valued function

- Differentiating a vector-valued function

- Theorem 12.1

Consider the vector-valued function $\mathbf{r}(t) = t\mathbf{i} + (4 - t^2)\mathbf{j}$.

(a) Sketch the graph of $\mathbf{r}(t)$. Use a graphing utility to verify your graph.

(b) Sketch the vectors $\mathbf{r}(1)$, $\mathbf{r}(1.25)$, and $\mathbf{r}(1.25) - \mathbf{r}(1)$ in the same coordinate system as the graph in part (a).

(c) Compare the vector $\mathbf{r}'(1)$ with the vector $\dfrac{\mathbf{r}(1.25) - \mathbf{r}(1)}{1.25 - 1}$.

Review the definition of the derivative of a vector-valued function and Theorem 12.1 (see page 828). After going over the solution, you can extend this exercise by asking students to sketch the vector $\mathbf{r}'(1)$. Students have trouble making similar sketches in Exercises 3–10.

Solution

(a) and (b) $\mathbf{r}(t) = t\mathbf{i} + (4 - t^2)\mathbf{j}$

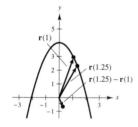

(c) $\qquad\qquad \mathbf{r}(1) = \mathbf{i} + 3\mathbf{j}$

$\qquad\qquad \mathbf{r}(1.25) = 1.25\mathbf{i} + 2.4375\mathbf{j}$

$\qquad \mathbf{r}(1.25) - \mathbf{r}(1) = 0.25\mathbf{i} - 0.5625\mathbf{j}$

$\qquad\qquad\qquad \mathbf{r}'(t) = \mathbf{i} - 2t\mathbf{j}$

$\qquad\qquad\qquad \mathbf{r}'(1) = \mathbf{i} - 2\mathbf{j}$

$\dfrac{\mathbf{r}(1.25) - \mathbf{r}(1)}{1.25 - 1} = \dfrac{0.25\mathbf{i} - 0.5625\mathbf{j}}{0.25} = \mathbf{i} - 2.25\mathbf{j}$

This vector approximates $\mathbf{r}'(1)$.

144

How Do You See It? Exercise

Page 835, Exercise 72 The graph shows a vector-valued function $\mathbf{r}(t)$ for $0 \le t \le 2\pi$ and its derivative $\mathbf{r}'(t)$ for several values of t.

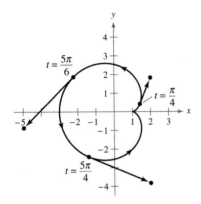

(a) For each derivative shown in the graph, determine whether each component is positive or negative.

(b) Is the curve smooth on the interval $[0, 2\pi]$? Explain.

Solution

(a) $t = \dfrac{\pi}{4}$: both components positive

$t = \dfrac{5\pi}{6}$: x-component negative, y-component positive

$t = \dfrac{5\pi}{4}$: x-component positive, y-component negative

(b) No. There is a cusp when $t = 0$ at $(1, 0)$.

Suggested Homework Assignment

Pages 834–835: 1, 5, 7, 9, 11–21 odd, 25, 27, 29, 35, 39–57 odd, and 69.

Section 12.3 Velocity and Acceleration

Section Comments

12.3 Velocity and Acceleration—Describe the velocity and acceleration associated with a vector-valued function. Use a vector-valued function to analyze projectile motion.

Teaching Tips

Stress to students that the velocity vector $\mathbf{v}$ gives the direction and the speed that a particle would travel if it flew off a curve at a certain time. In addition, $\|\mathbf{v}(t)\| = ds/dt$ is the rate of change of distance along the direction of motion with respect to time.

Note to students that the acceleration vector $\mathbf{a}(t)$ is not generally perpendicular to $\mathbf{v}(t)$.

You can use the sample problem below to review the following concepts:

- Describing the velocity associated with a vector-valued function

- Finding the speed of a particle moving on an elliptical path

- Describing the acceleration associated with a vector-valued function

145

Consider a particle moving on an elliptical path described by $\mathbf{r}(t) = a \sin \omega t\mathbf{i} + b \sin \omega t\mathbf{j}$, where $\omega = d\theta/dt$ is the constant angular velocity.

(a) Find the velocity vector. What is the speed of the particle?

(b) Find the acceleration vector and show that its direction is always toward the center of the ellipse.

Review the definitions of velocity and acceleration on page 837. Then go over the solution below.

Solution

$\mathbf{r}(t) = a \cos \omega t\mathbf{i} + b \sin \omega t\mathbf{j}$

(a) $\mathbf{r}'(t) = \mathbf{v}(t) = -a\omega \sin \omega t\mathbf{i} + b\omega \cos \omega t\mathbf{j}$

$\text{Speed} = \|\mathbf{v}(t)\| = \sqrt{a^2\omega^2 \sin^2 \omega t + b^2\omega^2 \cos^2 \omega t}$

(b) $\mathbf{a}(t) + \mathbf{v}'(t) = -a\omega^2 \cos \omega t\mathbf{i} + b\omega^2 \sin \omega t\mathbf{j}$

$= \omega^2(-a \cos \omega t\mathbf{i} - b \sin \omega t\mathbf{j})$

$= -\omega^2\mathbf{r}(t)$

How Do You See It? Exercise

Page 844, Exercise 58 The graph shows the path of a projectile and the velocity and acceleration vectors at times t_1 and t_2. Classify the angle between the velocity vector and the acceleration vector at times t_1 and t_2. Using the vectors, is the speed increasing or decreasing at times t_1 and t_2? Explain your reasoning.

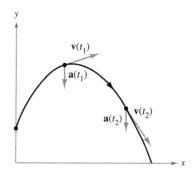

Solution

The angle at time t_1 is obtuse.

The angle at time t_2 is acute.

The speed is decreasing at time t_1 because the projectile is reaching its maximum height.

The speed is increasing at time t_2 because the object is accelerating due to gravity.

Suggested Homework Assignment

Pages 842–843: 1, 5, 7, 9, 13, 19, 23, 25, 27, 29, and 35.

Section 12.4 Tangent Vectors and Normal Vectors

Section Comments

12.4 **Tangent Vectors and Normal Vectors**—Find a unit tangent vector and a principal unit normal vector at a point on a space curve. Find the tangential and normal components of acceleration.

Teaching Tips

Use Exercise 43 to review the following concepts:

- Describing the velocity and acceleration associated with a vector-valued function

- Finding a unit tangent vector

- Finding a principal unit normal vector (if it exists)

If necessary, review velocity and acceleration in Section 12.3. Go over the definitions of the unit tangent vector (see page 845) and the principal unit normal vector (see page 846). Then go over the solution below.

Solution

$\mathbf{r}(t) = 3t\mathbf{i} + 4t\mathbf{j}$

$\mathbf{v}(t) = \mathbf{r}'(t) = 3\mathbf{i} + 4\mathbf{j}, \|\mathbf{v}(t)\| = \sqrt{9 + 16} = 5$

$\mathbf{a}(t) = \mathbf{v}'(t) = \mathbf{0}$

$\mathbf{T}(t) = \dfrac{\mathbf{v}(t)}{\|\mathbf{v}(t)\|} = \dfrac{3}{5}\mathbf{i} + \dfrac{4}{5}\mathbf{j}$

$\mathbf{T}'(t) = 0 \implies \mathbf{N}(t)$ does not exist.

The path is a line. The speed is constant (5).

How Do You See It? Exercise

Page 853, Exercise 44 The figures show the paths of two particles.

(i)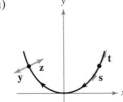

(ii)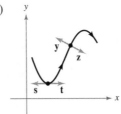

(a) Which vector, **s** or **t**, represents the unit tangent vector? Explain.

(b) Which vector, **y** or **z**, represents the principal unit normal vector? Explain.

Solution

(a) (i) The vector **s** represents the unit tangent vector because it points in the direction of motion.

    (ii) The vector **t** represents the unit tangent vector because it points in the direction of motion.

147

(b) (i) The vector $\mathbf{z}$ represents the unit normal vector because it points in the direction that the curve is bending.

(ii) The vector $\mathbf{z}$ represents the unit normal vector because it points in the direction that the curve is bending.

Suggested Homework Assignment

Pages 852–854: 1, 5, 11, 13, 15, 19, 23, 27, 37, 59, and 69.

Section 12.5 Arc Length and Curvature

Section Comments

12.5   **Arc Length and Curvature**—Find the arc length of a space curve. Use the arc length parameter to describe a plane curve or space curve. Find the curvature of a curve at a point on the curve. Use a vector-valued function to find frictional force.

Teaching Tips

You may wish to use the following method to intuitively describe curvature:

$$K = \frac{\|\mathbf{T}'(t)\|}{\|\mathbf{r}'(t)\|},$$

since the length of $\mathbf{T}$ is constant, $\|\mathbf{T}(t)\|$ is the rate of change of direction of the unit tangent vector and $\|\mathbf{r}(t)\|$ measures the speed along the curve. So, K is the ratio of the rate of change in the tangent vector $\mathbf{T}$ to the rate of change in arc length.

Point out to the class that since the unit vector satisfies $\|\mathbf{T}(t)\| = 1$, $\mathbf{T}'(t)$ is perpendicular to $\mathbf{T}(t)$ and so

$$\mathbf{N}(t) = \frac{\mathbf{T}'(t)}{\|\mathbf{T}(t)\|}$$

is perpendicular to $\mathbf{T}(t)$. So, $\mathbf{N}(t)$ is the unit normal vector.

Use Exercise 62 to review the following concepts:

- Finding the arc length of a space curve

- Theorem 12.6

- Finding the curvature of a plane curve at a point on the curve

- Theorem 12.9

- Analyzing the curvature of a curve

Go over Theorem 12.6 and part (a). If you wish to skip the integration steps, show your students how to set up the integral and then use a graphing utility or computer algebra system to find the result. Then go over the definition of curvature (see page 858) and Theorem 12.9 (see page 860). Note in part (b) that we use the rectangular equations that correspond to the given vector-valued function.

Solution

$\mathbf{r}(t) = t\mathbf{i} + t^2\mathbf{j}$

(a) $\dfrac{dx}{dt} = 1$, $\dfrac{dy}{dt} = 2t$

$$s = \int_0^2 \sqrt{1 + 4t^2}\, dt = \frac{1}{2} \int_0^2 \sqrt{1 + 4t^2}(2)\, dt \quad (u = 2t)$$

$$= \frac{1}{2} \cdot \frac{1}{2} \left[2t\sqrt{1 + 4t^2} + \ln\left|2t + \sqrt{1 + 4t^2}\right| \right]_0^2 \quad \text{(Theorem 8.2)}$$

$$= \frac{1}{4}\left[4\sqrt{17} + \ln\left|4 + \sqrt{17}\right| \right] \approx 4.647$$

(b) Let $y = x^2$, $y' = 2x$, $y'' = 2$.

At $t = 0$, $x = 0$, $y = 0$, $y' = 0$, $y'' = 2$.

$$K = \frac{2}{[1 + 0]^{3/2}} = 2$$

At $t = 1$, $x = 1$, $y = 1$, $y' = 2$, $y'' = 2$.

$$K = \frac{2}{[1 + (2)^2]^{3/2}} = \frac{2}{5^{3/2}} \approx 0.179$$

At $t = 2$, $x = 2$, $y = 4$, $y' = 4$, $y'' = 2$.

$$K = \frac{2}{[1 + 16]^{3/2}} = \frac{2}{17^{3/2}} \approx 0.0285$$

(c) As t changes from 0 to 2, the curvature decreases.

How Do You See It? Exercise

Page 865, Exercise 64 Using the graph of the ellipse, at what point(s) is the curvature the least and the greatest?

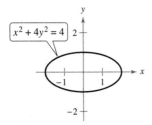

Solution

From the shape of the ellipse, you see that the curvature is greatest at the endpoints of the major axis, $(\pm 2, 0)$, and least at the endpoints of the minor axis, $(0, \pm 1)$.

Suggested Homework Assignment

Pages 864–865: 1, 5, 13, 21, 25, 27, 29, 33, 37, 43, and 65.

Chapter 12 Project

Throwing a Shot

The path of a shot thrown during a shot put competition at an angle θ is

$$\mathbf{r}(t) = (v_0 \cos \theta)t\mathbf{i} + \left[h + (v_0 \sin \theta)t - \tfrac{1}{2}gt^2\right]\mathbf{j}$$

where v_0 is the initial speed, h is the initial height, t is the time in seconds, and $g \approx 32$ feet per second per second is the acceleration due to gravity. (This formula neglects air resistance.)

Exercises

In Exercises 1–5, a shot is thrown from an initial height of 6 feet with an initial velocity of 40 feet per second and an initial angle of 35°.

1. Find the vector-valued function $\mathbf{r}(t)$ that gives the position of the shot.

2. At what time is the shot at its maximum height?

3. What is the maximum height of the shot?

4. How long is the shot in the air?

5. What is the horizontal distance traveled by the shot?

In Exercises 6–10, a shot is thrown from an initial height of 6 feet with an initial velocity of 40 feet per second and an initial angle of 45°.

6. Find the vector-valued function $\mathbf{r}(t)$ that gives the position of the shot.

7. At what time is the shot at its maximum height?

8. What is the maximum height of the shot?

9. How long is the shot in the air?

10. What is the horizontal distance traveled by the shot?

11. Write an equation for t, the time when a shot thrown from an initial height h with an initial velocity of v_0 and an initial angle of θ hits the ground.

12. Write an equation for the horizontal distance traveled by a shot thrown from an initial height h with an initial velocity of v_0 and an initial angle of θ.

In Exercises 13 and 14, a shot is thrown from an initial height of 6 feet with an initial velocity of 40 feet per second.

13. Write an equation for the time t when the shot hits the ground in terms of θ, the angle at which it is thrown.

14. Write an equation for the horizontal distance traveled by the shot in terms of θ.

15. Use a graphing utility to graph the equation you wrote in Exercise 14. Where does the maximum occur? What does this mean in the context of the problem?

Chapter 13 Functions of Several Variables

Chapter Comments

The terminology used for functions of several variables parallels functions of one variable. So, a discussion of domain, independent and dependent variables, composite functions, and polynomial and rational functions should move quickly. Graphing functions of several variables is difficult for most students, so be sure to note the comment after Example 2 on using traces in planes parallel to the coordinate planes on page 874.

Discussion of level curves and contour maps, as on pages 875 and 876, is often meaningful to your students since many have seen a topographic map depicting high mountains or deep oceans.

Unless you are taking a theoretic approach to the course, don't get bogged down in the ε-δ definition of the limit of a function of two variables in Section 13.2. Point out that limits of functions of several variables have the same properties regarding sums, differences, products, and quotients as do limits of functions of one variable. Go over Example 4 on page 887 with your students and be sure to point out that in order for a limit of a function of several variables to exist, the limit must be the same along *all* possible approaches.

A discussion of continuity for functions of several variables should parallel your discussion of continuity from Chapter 1.

Be sure to have students memorize the definitions of partial derivatives for a function of several variables. Otherwise, a partial derivative won't mean anything to them. If possible, show a video depicting a geometric interpretation of a partial derivative when applied to a function of two independent variables.

Hopefully, your students already understand that for a function of a single variable, a differential is an approximation for a change in the function value. This concept is generalized in Section 13.4. Examples 3 and 4 (pages 906 and 907, respectively), showing how the total differential is used to approximate a change in the function value, are important.

Be careful of notation when discussing the Chain Rules in Section 13.5. Many students are careless about the notation and easily mix up dy/dx and $\partial y/\partial x$. Implicit differentiation seems confusing to many students. You may want to slowly and carefully go over this idea.

Sections 13.6 through 13.10 consider some applications of the partial derivative. As you begin Section 13.6 with the discussion of the directional derivative and the gradient, be sure that your students understand that a gradient is a vector, hence, the boldface print, ∇f. It is important for your students to understand the difference between $\nabla f(x, y)$, a vector in the xy-plane, and $\nabla F(x, y, z)$, a vector in space. For a function of two independent variables, the gradient is normal to the level curves in the same plane as the curves, whereas for a function of three independent variables, the gradient, ∇F, is normal to the surface $F(x, y, z) = 0$. This concept is brought out in Section 13.7 with the discussion of tangent planes and normal lines to a surface.

Section 13.8 examines extrema in space. The ideas and terminology again parallel what was done in the plane. Be sure to note that critical points occur where *one* partial derivative is undefined or when *both* partials are zero. The idea of a saddle point may be new to your students. The Second Partials Test for extrema is great when it works. However, point out to your students that similar to the Second Derivative Test for functions of one variable, it can fail. Example 4 on page 944 demonstrates this case. The method of least squares, discussed in Section 13.9 could be skipped if time is a problem. In order to solve extrema problems using Lagrange multipliers, Section 13.10, your students need to solve simultaneous equations. Encourage them to be creative in this regard.

Section 13.1 Introduction to Functions of Several Variables

Section Comments

13.1   Introduction to Functions of Several Variables—Understand the notation for a function of several variables. Sketch the graph of a function of two variables. Sketch level curves for a function of two variables. Sketch level surfaces for a function of three variables. Use computer graphics to graph a function of two variables.

Teaching Tips

As an introduction to this section, ask students to think back on the mathematics they have seen up to this point and ask where they have seen functions of two variables before. You can remind students that Work $= FD$ is an example of a function of two variables and so is Area $= lw$. You can also point out that Volume $= lwh$ is an example of a function in three variables.

Be sure to make comparisons to functions that students have seen before when dealing with R^3. For example, the unit circle $x^2 + y^2 = 1$ will be a circular cylinder in R^3. You may want to work out Example 2 with the class.

If you have access to Mathematica, many examples can be done going from R^2 to R^3. You may want to present the various pictures and the level curves given on page 879.

We suggest Exercise 66 to review the following concepts:

- Definition of a function of two variables

- Sketching the graph of a function of two variables

- Transformations of the graph of a function of two variables

Go over the definition of a function of two variables on page 872 and the graph of a function of two variables on page 874. Students will need to know this material in the remaining chapters. Sketch the graph of the function. You may want to show students how to use a graphing utility or a computer algebra system to graph the function. Parts (b)–(d) involve transformations of the graph of a function of two variables, similar to a function of a single variable (see Section P.3). In part (e), note that the value of y for $z = f(x, x)$ is restricted to x. So, the graph of $z = f(x, x)$ is the intersection of the plane $y = x$ and $f(x, y) = xy$ for $x \geq 0$ and $y \geq 0$.

Solution

$f(x, y) = xy, x \geq 0, y \geq 0$

(a)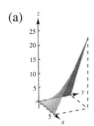

(b) g is a vertical translation of f three units downward.

(c) g is a reflection of f in the xy-plane.

(d) The graph of g is lower than the graph of f. If $z = f(x, y)$ is on the graph of f, then $\frac{1}{2}z$ is on the graph of g.

(e)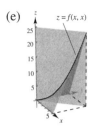
$z = f(x, x)$

How Do You See It? Exercise

Page 883, Exercise 90 The contour map of the Southern Hemisphere shown in the figure was computer generated using data collected by satellite instrumentation. Color is used to show the "ozone hole" in Earth's atmosphere. The purple and blue areas represent the lowest levels of ozone, and the green areas represent the highest levels. *(Source: NASA)*

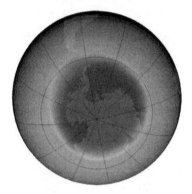

(a) Do the level curves correspond to equally spaced ozone levels? Explain.

(b) Describe how to obtain a more detailed contour map.

Solution

(a) No; the level curves are uneven and sporadically spaced.

(b) Use more colors.

Suggested Homework Assignment

Pages 880–881: 1, 3, 15, 21–31 odd, 35–41 odd, 47, 49, 53.

Section 13.2 Limits and Continuity

Section Comments

13.2 **Limits and Continuity**—Understand the definition of a neighborhood in the plane. Understand and use the definition of the limit of a function of two variables. Extend the concept of continuity to a function of two variables. Extend the concept of continuity to a function of three variables.

Teaching Tips

Begin the lesson by stressing to students that while the definitions of limits and continuity will look very familiar to those in multivariable functions, behaviors of these functions will be different.

When dealing with limits of two- or three-variable functions, it will not be enough to say the limit of $f(x, y)$ or $f(x, y, z)$ as (x_0, y_0) or (x_0, y_0, z_0) approaches (x, y) or (x, y, z) on the x-, y-, or z-axes, so you need to choose independent paths. As with single-variable functions, sometimes, direct substitution can be used, which may not result in division by zero, as in $\lim_{(x, y) \to (1, -2)} (x^2 + 3y)$. As in Example 4, direct substitution can't be used. Stress to students that they must choose paths as shown in Example 4 to arrive at the conclusion that the limit does not exist.

Another good example to show students is $\lim_{(x, y) \to (0, 0)} \dfrac{x^2 - y^2}{x^2 + y^2}$.

This will show students the method and importance of path independence.

Introduce the use of polar coordinates by trying to find $\lim_{(x, y) \to (0, 0)} \dfrac{x^2 y^2}{\sqrt{x^2 + y^2}}$.

Motivate students to recall L'Hôpital's Rule by working out Exercise 58.

We recommend Exercises 37 and 38 to review the following concepts:

- The definition of the limit of a function of two variables

- Using the definition of the limit of a function of two variables

The existence or nonexistence of $f(x, y)$ at $(x, y) = (c_1, c_2)$ has no bearing on the existence of the limit of $f(x, y)$ as (x, y) approaches (c_1, c_2).

In addition to the solution given below, you could ask students for an example where the limit exists but the function does not, and an example where the limit and the function both exist. Example 3 is a case where the limit exists but the function does not, and Example 2 is a case where the limit and the function both exist.

Solution

37. No. The existence of $f(2, 3)$ has no bearing on the existence of the limit as $(x, y) \to (2, 3)$.

38. No. $f(2, 3)$ can equal any number, or not even be defined.

How Do You See It? Exercise

Page 891, Exercise 40 The figure shows the graph of $f(x, y) = \ln(x^2 + y^2)$. From the graph, does it appear that the limit at each point exists?

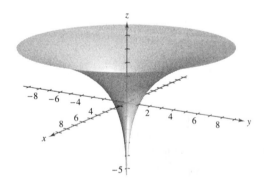

(a) $(-1, -1)$ (b) $(0, 3)$ (c) $(0, 0)$ (d) $(2, 0)$

Solution

The limit appears to exist at all the points except (c) $(0, 0)$. Near this point, the graph tends to $-\infty$.

Suggested Homework Assignment

Pages 891–893: 1, 17, 19, 21, 27, 31, 43, 53, 55, 57, 59, 61, 63, 67, 79, and 81.

Section 13.3 Partial Derivatives

Section Comments

13.3 **Partial Derivatives**—Find and use partial derivatives of a function of two variables. Find and use partial derivatives of a function of three or more variables. Find higher-order partial derivatives of a function of two or three variables.

Teaching Tips

One key idea students must understand in this section is the idea of a function being continuous will play a vital role. Be sure to stress Theorem 13.3.

Another key idea to discuss with students is that the derivative of a constant is zero. As you go through examples finding partial derivatives, inform students that when taking the partial derivative in terms of x, hold all other variables constant; when taking the partial derivative in terms of y, hold all other variables constant, and so forth.

Point out the various notations for partial derivatives. Note to students that when finding

$$\frac{\partial^3 f}{\partial y^2 \partial x} = f_{xyy},$$

they are first finding the partial derivative in terms of x and then finding the partial derivative twice in terms of y.

We suggest using the sample problem below to review the following concepts:

- Finding partial derivatives of a function of two variables

- Finding higher-order partial derivatives of a function of two variables

- Theorem 13.3

Find the four second partial derivatives of the function $f(x, y) = \sin(x - 2y)$. Show that the second mixed partial derivatives f_{xy} and f_{yx} are equal.

Go over as much as you feel is necessary, such as the definition of partial derivatives of a function of two variables, notation for first partial derivatives, higher-order partial derivatives, and Theorem 13.3. Keep in mind that understanding this material is key for students to succeed in the remaining chapters.

Solution

$f(x, y) = \sin(x - 2y)$

$f_x(x, y) = \cos(x - 2y)$

$f_{xx}(x, y) = -\sin(x - 2y)$

$f_{xy}(x, y) = 2\sin(x - 2y)$

$f_y(x, y) = -2\cos(x - 2y)$

$f_{yy}(x, y) = -4\sin(x - 2y)$

$f_{yx}(x, y) = 2\sin(x - 2y)$

So, $f_{xy}(x, y) = f_{yx}(x, y)$.

155

How Do You See It? Exercise

Page 902, Exercise 114 Use the graph of the surface to determine the sign of each partial derivative. Explain your reasoning.

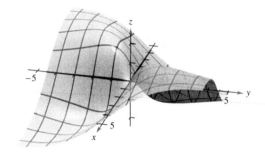

(a) $f_x(4, 1)$

(b) $f_y(4, 1)$

(c) $f_x(-1, -2)$

(d) $f_y(-1, -2)$

Solution

(a) $f_x(4, 1) < 0$

(b) $f_y(4, 1) > 0$

(c) $f_x(-1, -2) < 0$

(d) $f_y(-1, -2) > 0$

Suggested Homework Assignment

Pages 900–903: 1, 3, 13, 23, 25, 27, 35, 49, 51, 55, 57, 61, 65, 67, 71, 81, 83, 93, and 129.

Section 13.4 Differentials

Section Comments

13.4   **Differentials**—Understand the concepts of increments and differentials. Extend the concept of differentiability to a function of two variables. Use a differential as an approximation.

Teaching Tips

Begin the lesson by asking students if they believe that a function f is differentiable at (x_0, y_0) but f_x and f_y do not exist at (x_0, y_0). In addition, ask students if they believe that a function f is nondifferentiable at (x_0, y_0) even though f_x and f_y exist at (x_0, y_0). Lead students to the answers of no for the first question and yes for the second.

Differentiability must be discussed in this section using the definition.

Ask students to consider $f(x, y) = \begin{cases} \dfrac{(x-y)^2}{x^2 + y^2}, & (x, y) \neq (0, 0) \\ 1, & (x, y) = (0, 0) \end{cases}$.

This is a good example that shows nondifferentiability.

You may want to work out Example 2 using the definition of differentiability to show $f(x, y) = x^2 + 3y$ is differentiable at every point in the plane.

When using a differential as an approximation, you could show Example 3 to the students.

Although we made changes to the section exercises, no changes were made based on the data.

156

We suggest the sample problem below to review the following concepts:

- Finding the increment of z, Δz

- Finding the total differential for a function, dz

Consider the function $f(x, y) = \sqrt{x^2 + y^2}$.

(a) Evaluate $f(3, 1)$ and $f(3.05, 1.1)$.

(b) Use the results of part (a) to calculate Δz.

(c) Use the total differential dz to approximate Δz. Compare your result with that of part (b).

Go over increments and differentials on page 904 and approximation by differentials on page 906.

Solution

$f(x, y) = \sqrt{x^2 + y^2}$

(a) $f(3, 1) = \sqrt{9 + 1} = \sqrt{10} \approx 3.1623$

$\quad\quad f(3.05, 1.1) = \sqrt{3.05^2 + 1.1^2} \approx 3.2423$

(b) $\Delta z = f(3.05, 1.1) - f(3, 1) \approx 0.0800$

(c) $dz = \dfrac{x}{\sqrt{x^2 + y^2}}\, dx + \dfrac{y}{\sqrt{x^2 + y^2}}\, dy$

$\quad\quad = \dfrac{3}{\sqrt{10}}(0.05) + \dfrac{1}{\sqrt{10}}(0.1) \approx 0.0791$

$\quad \Delta z \approx dz$

How Do You See It? Exercise

Page 909, Exercise 20 Which point has a greater differential, $(2, 2)$ or $\left(\frac{1}{2}, \frac{1}{2}\right)$? Explain. (Assume that dx and dy are the same for both points.)

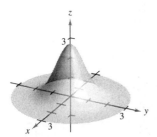

Solution

The differential is greater at $\left(\frac{1}{2}, \frac{1}{2}\right)$ than at $(2, 2)$ because the surface is increasing faster there.

Suggested Homework Assignment

Pages 909–910: 1, 7, 11, 17, 23, 35, and 39.

Section 13.5 Chain Rules for Functions of Several Variables

Section Comments

13.5   **Chain Rules for Functions of Several Variables**—Use the Chain Rules for functions of several variables. Find partial derivatives implicitly.

Teaching Tips

Important things to stress for this lesson are to show students how the Chain Rule for a function of one variable can now be extended to multivariable functions, the use of tree diagrams, and implicit differentiation.

Be sure to carefully review the differences between the Chain Rule of one independent variable and two or more independent variables.

Good examples to show students using tree diagrams are:

Example 1: Let $z = 2xy^3 + x^2y^2$, where $x = \sin t$ and $y = \cos(4t)$, find dz/dt.

Example 2: Let $z = 2xy^3 + x^2y^2$, where $x = te^{5s}$ and $y = 2te^{-5s}$, find $\partial z/\partial s$ and $\partial z/\partial t$.

You may want to work out Example 2 in the text with the class to prove an application. You may also want to work out Example 7 to show students implicit differentiation.

We suggest the sample problem below to review the following concepts:

- Chain Rules for functions of several variables

- Product Rule for differentiation

Consider the function $f(x, y, z) = xyz$, where $x = t^2$, $y = 2t$, and $z = e^{-t}$.

(a) Use the appropriate Chain Rule to find df/dt.

(b) Write f as a function of t and then find df/dt. Explain why this result is the same as that of part (a).

Review Theorem 13.6 and note that it can be extended to any number of variables (see page 911). So, you can write the Chain Rule shown in part (a) of the solution. Be careful of notation in this section, as many students easily mix up dy/dx and $\partial y/\partial x$. After rewriting f in part (b), you can use single-variable techniques to find df/dt. (If needed, review the Product Rule in Section 2.3.) Note that the results are the same because the two methods for calculating the derivative are equivalent.

Solution

$f(x, y, z) = xyz, \ x = t^2, \ y = 2t, \ z = e^{-t}$

(a) $\dfrac{df}{dt} = \dfrac{\partial f}{\partial x}\dfrac{dx}{dt} + \dfrac{\partial f}{\partial y}\dfrac{dy}{dt} + \dfrac{\partial f}{\partial z}\dfrac{dz}{dt}$

$\qquad = yz(2t) + xz(2) + xy(-e^{-t})$

$\qquad = 4t^2e^{-t} + 2t^2e^{-t} - 2t^3e^{-t} = 2t^2e^{-t}(3 - t)$

(b) $f = t^2(2t)(e^{-t}) = 2t^3e^{-t}$

$\qquad \dfrac{df}{dt} = -2t^3e^{-t} + 6t^2e^{-t} = 2t^2e^{-t}(3 - t)$

The results are the same.

How Do You See It? Exercise

Page 918, Exercise 48 The path of an object represented by $w = f(x, y)$ is shown, where x and y are functions of t. The point on the graph represents the position of the object.

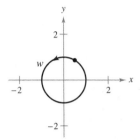

Determine whether each of the following is positive, negative, or zero.

(a) $\dfrac{dx}{dt}$ (b) $\dfrac{dy}{dt}$

Solution

(a) $\dfrac{dx}{dt} < 0$ (moving to the left)

(b) $\dfrac{dy}{dt} > 0$ (moving upward)

Suggested Homework Assignment

Page 917: 1, 5, 9, 11, 15, 17, 21, 23, 31, and 35.

Section 13.6 Directional Derivatives and Gradients

Section Comments

13.6   **Directional Derivatives and Gradients**—Find and use directional derivatives of a function of two variables. Find the gradient of a function of two variables. Use the gradient of a function of two variables in applications. Find directional derivatives and gradients of functions of three variables.

Teaching Tips

The key ideas to point out to students in this section are the computation and geometric meaning of the directional derivative; the computation and geometric meaning of the gradient vector; and the relationships among tangent planes, gradient vectors, and directional derivatives.

Point out to students that a gradient vector has many meanings. It is a normal vector to a surface in R^3, it is in the direction of the greatest change of a surface at a point, it is a perpendicular vector to contour curves and a surface, and it is a vector with a length equal to the maximum value of the directional derivative.

You may want to ask students if they understand the following: If $D_{\mathbf{u}} f(x, y) = \nabla f(x, y)\mathbf{u}$, where $\mathbf{u}$ is a unit vector, why does this represent the directional derivative in the direction of $\mathbf{u}$ as the projection of the gradient vector onto $\mathbf{u}$?

When defining the definition of gradient, be sure to use a figure similar to Figure 13.48 on page 922. If possible, use a computer algebra system.

159

Be sure to follow up with applications such as Examples 5 and 6 to illustrate how much information the gradient provides. If accessible, use a computer algebra system to illustrate the solutions.

We suggest using Exercise 48 to review the following concepts:

- Sketching the graph of a function of two variables

- Finding the directional derivative of a function (Theorem 13.9)

- Finding the gradient of a function

- Discussing properties of the gradient

If needed, you can review sketching the graph of a function of two variables in Section 13.1. Go over Theorem 13.9 and find the directional derivatives in part (b) and, if time permits, part (c). Go over the definition of the gradient of a function of two variables (see page 922) and be sure your students understand that a gradient is a vector. In part (d), note that $f_x(x, y) = -2x$ and $f_y(x, y) = -2y$. When discussing the geometric meaning of the result in part (f), note that ∇f is the direction of greatest rate of change of f. So, in a direction orthogonal to ∇f, the rate of change of f is 0.

Solution

(a) $f(x, y) = 9 - x^2 - y^2$

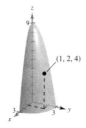

(b) $D_{\mathbf{u}} f(x, y) = -2x \cos \theta - 2y \sin \theta$

$D_{\mathbf{u}} f(1, 2) = -2 \cos \theta - 4 \sin \theta$

(i) $\theta = -\dfrac{\pi}{4}$, $D_{\mathbf{u}} f(1, 2) = -2\left(\dfrac{\sqrt{2}}{2}\right) - 4\left(\dfrac{\sqrt{2}}{2}\right) = \sqrt{2}$

(ii) $\theta = \dfrac{\pi}{3}$, $D_{\mathbf{u}} f(1, 2) = -2\left(\dfrac{1}{2}\right) - 4\left(\dfrac{\sqrt{3}}{2}\right) = -1 - 2\sqrt{3}$

(iii) $\theta = \dfrac{3\pi}{4}$, $D_{\mathbf{u}} f(1, 2) = -2\left(-\dfrac{\sqrt{2}}{2}\right) - 4\left(\dfrac{\sqrt{2}}{2}\right) = -\sqrt{2}$

(iv) $\theta = -\dfrac{\pi}{2}$, $D_{\mathbf{u}} f(1, 2) = -2(0) - 4(-1) = 4$

(c) (i) $\mathbf{v} = 3\mathbf{i} + \mathbf{j}$, $\mathbf{u} = \dfrac{1}{\sqrt{10}}(3\mathbf{i} + \mathbf{j})$

$D_{\mathbf{u}} f(1, 2) = (-2\mathbf{i} - 4\mathbf{j}) \cdot \left[\dfrac{1}{\sqrt{10}}(3\mathbf{i} + \mathbf{j})\right] = \dfrac{1}{\sqrt{10}}(-10) = -\sqrt{10}$

(ii) $\mathbf{v} = -8\mathbf{i} - 6\mathbf{j}$, $\mathbf{u} = -\dfrac{4}{5}\mathbf{i} - \dfrac{3}{5}\mathbf{j}$

$D_{\mathbf{u}} f(1, 2) = (-2\mathbf{i} - 4\mathbf{j}) \cdot \left(-\dfrac{4}{5}\mathbf{i} - \dfrac{3}{5}\mathbf{j}\right) = 4$

160

(iii) $\mathbf{v} = 4\mathbf{i} + 6\mathbf{j}$, $\mathbf{u} = \dfrac{1}{\sqrt{13}}(2\mathbf{i} + 3\mathbf{j})$

$$D_{\mathbf{u}}f(1, 2) = (-2\mathbf{i} - 4\mathbf{j}) \cdot \left[\dfrac{1}{\sqrt{13}}(2\mathbf{i} + 3\mathbf{j})\right] = \dfrac{-16}{\sqrt{13}}$$

(iv) $\mathbf{v} = 3\mathbf{i} + 3\mathbf{j}$, $\mathbf{u} = \dfrac{1}{\sqrt{2}}(\mathbf{i} + \mathbf{j})$

$$D_{\mathbf{u}}f(1, 2) = (-2\mathbf{i} - 4\mathbf{j}) \cdot \left[\dfrac{1}{\sqrt{2}}(\mathbf{i} + \mathbf{j})\right] = -\dfrac{6}{\sqrt{2}} = -3\sqrt{2}$$

(d) $\nabla f(1, 2) = -2\mathbf{i} - 4\mathbf{j}$

(e) $\|\nabla f(1, 2)\| = \sqrt{4 + 16} = \sqrt{20} = 2\sqrt{5}$, maximum

(f) $\mathbf{u} = \dfrac{1}{\sqrt{5}}(-2\mathbf{i} + \mathbf{j})$ is orthogonal to $\nabla f(1, 2)$.

$$D_{\mathbf{u}}f(1, 2) = \nabla f(1, 2) \cdot \mathbf{u} = 0$$

The rate of change is 0 in the direction orthogonal to $\nabla f(1, 2)$.

How Do You See It? Exercise

Page 930, Exercise 54 The figure shows a topographic map carried by a group of hikers. Sketch the paths of steepest descent when the hikers start at point A and when they start at point B. (To print an enlarged copy of the graph, go to *MathGraphs.com*.)

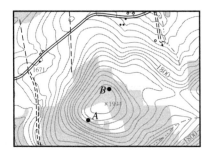

Solution

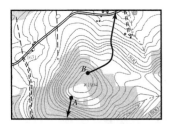

Suggested Homework Assignment

Pages 928–930: 1, 5, 9, 13, 17, 23, 25, 31, 37, 47, 55, 57, 59, 61, and 63.

Section 13.7 Tangent Planes and Normal Lines

Section Comments

13.7 **Tangent Planes and Normal Lines**—Find equations of tangent planes and normal lines to surfaces. Find the angle of inclination of a plane in space. Compare the gradients $\nabla f(x, y)$ and $\nabla F(x, y, z)$.

Teaching Tips

Begin the lesson by talking about the billiard ball and normal lines as outlined in the Exploration on page 931. This will set the stage for the topics in this section.

When working out examples with the students, it would be useful to have access to a computer algebra system to illustrate the surfaces and the tangent planes. Make the connection between equations of tangent lines in R^2 with equations of tangent planes to surfaces in R^3. Illustrate how you must use the gradient to find these tangent planes.

We suggest the sample problem below to review the following concepts:

- Finding an equation of a tangent plane to a surface

- Theorem 13.13

- Finding an equation of a normal line to a surface

Consider the elliptic cone given by $x^2 - y^2 + z^2 = 0$.

(a) Find an equation of the tangent plane at the point $(5, 13, -12)$.

(b) Find symmetric equations of the normal line at the point $(5, 13, -12)$.

Go over the definitions of tangent plane and normal line and Theorem 13.13 on page 932. Then go over the solution.

Solution

(a) $x^2 - y^2 + z^2 = 0$, $(5, 13, -12)$

$F(x, y, z) = x^2 - y^2 + z^2$

$F_x(x, y, z) = 2x$ $\qquad$ $F_y(x, y, z) = -2y$ $\qquad$ $F_z(x, y, z) = 2z$

$F_x(5, 13, -12) = 10$ $\qquad$ $F_y(5, 13, -12) = -26$ $\qquad$ $F_z(5, 13, -12) = -24$

Direction numbers: $5, -13, -12$

Plane: $5(x - 5) - 13(y - 13) - 12(z + 12) = 0$

$\qquad\qquad\qquad\qquad\qquad 5x - 13y - 12z = 0$

(b) Line: $\dfrac{x - 5}{5} = \dfrac{y - 13}{-13} = \dfrac{z + 12}{-12}$

How Do You See It? Exercise

Page 938, Exercise 52 The graph shows the ellipsoid $x^2 + 4y^2 + z^2 = 16$. Use the graph to determine the equation of the tangent plane at each of the given points.

(a) $(4, 0, 0)$ (b) $(0, -2, 0)$ (c) $(0, 0, -4)$

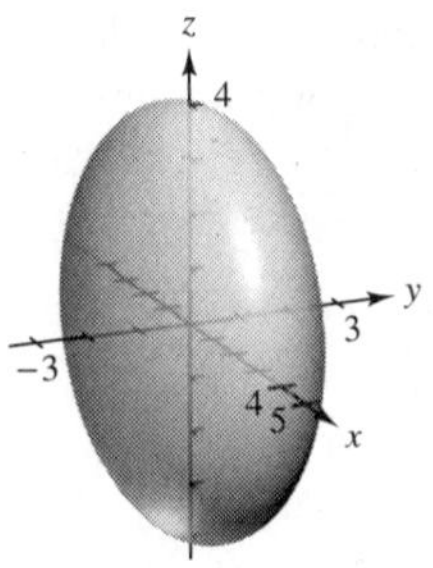

Solution

(a) At $(4, 0, 0)$, the tangent plane is parallel to the yz-plane.

  Equation: $x = 4$

(b) At $(0, -2, 0)$, the tangent plane is parallel to the xz-plane.

  Equation: $y = -2$

(c) At $(0, 0, -4)$, the tangent plane is parallel to the xy-plane.

Suggested Homework Assignment

Pages 937–938: 1, 5, 7, 11, 13, 15, 19, 23, 27, 31, 33, 39, 43, 45, 49, and 55.

Section 13.8 Extrema of Functions of Two Variables

Section Comments

13.8   **Extrema of Functions of Two Variables**—Find absolute and relative extrema of a function of two variables. Use the Second Partials Test to find relative extrema of a function of two variables.

Teaching Tips

All of the previous topics covered regarding finding extrema of a function of a single variable in R^2 will now be extended to finding extrema in R^3. Some important points to stress to students are that critical numbers will now be (x_0, y_0, z_0) and so will the extrema. Make use of the illustrations given on page 941.

You may want to show that given a function such as $f(x, y) = x^4 + y^4$, there is no information given about the extrema when $d = 0$.

We suggest using Exercise 53 to review the following concepts:

- Showing that a function has a critical point

- Analyzing the behavior of a function at a critical point

- Theorems 13.15–13.17

- Definition of relative extrema

- Saddle point

Note that the ideas and terminology parallel what was done in the plane. Go over the definition of critical point (see page 941). After doing part (a), review the definition of relative extrema and Theorems 13.15–13.17. Go over part (b) and use the following figures given on the transparencies to reinforce the results. The idea of a saddle point may be new to your students.

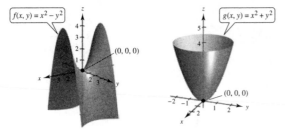

Solution

$f(x, y) = x^2 - y^2$, $g(x, y) = x^2 + y^2$

(a) $f_x = 2x = 0$, $f_y = -2y = 0 \implies (0, 0)$ is a critical point.

$g_x = 2x = 0$, $g_y = 2y = 0 \implies (0, 0)$ is a critical point.

(b) $f_{xx} = 2$, $f_{yy} = -2$, $f_{xy} = 0$

$d = 2(-2) - 0 < 0 \implies (0, 0)$ is a saddle point.

$g_{xx} = 2$, $g_{yy} = 2$, $g_{xy} = 0$

$d = 2(2) - 0 > 0 \implies (0, 0)$ is a relative minimum.

How Do You See It? Exercise

Page 947, Exercise 54 Determine whether each labeled point is an absolute maximum, an absolute minimum, or neither.

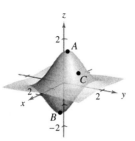

Solution

A is an absolute maximum.

B is an absolute minimum.

C is neither.

Suggested Homework Assignment

Pages 946–947: 1, 7, 9, 15, 17, 23, 31, 33, 39, 43, 55, and 57.

Section 13.9 Applications of Extrema

Section Comments

13.9   Applications of Extrema—Solve optimization problems involving functions of several variables. Use the method of least squares.

Teaching Tips

As in Example 1 in the text, ask students to recall the function $x + y + z = 1$, which is a tetrahedron. Draw this either on the board or using a computer algebra system with a box resting inside of the tetrahedron. Work out with students how to find the maximum volume of the box.

Work out Example 2 with the class. This will give students an application on how to maximize profit. If there is time, you may also want to cover Example 3.

We suggest the sample problem below to review the following concept:

- Solving an optimization problem

The sum of the length and the girth (perimeter of a cross section) of a package carried by a delivery service cannot exceed 108 inches. Find the dimensions of the rectangular package of largest volume that may be sent.

Use the following figure to illustrate girth.

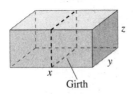

Solution

Let x, y, and z be the length, width, and height, respectively. Then the sum of the length and girth is given by $x + (2y + 2z) = 108$ or $x = 108 - 2y - 2z$. The volume is given by

$$V = xyz = 108zy - 2zy^2 - 2yz^2$$

$$V_y = 108z - 4yz - 2z^2 = z(108 - 4y - 2z) = 0$$

$$V_z = 108y - 2y^2 - 4yz = y(108 - 2y - 4z) = 0.$$

Solving the system $4y + 2z = 108$ and $2y + 4z = 108$, you obtain the solution $x = 36$ inches, $y = 18$ inches, and $z = 18$ inches.

How Do You See It? Exercise

Page 954, Exercise 32 Match the regression equation with the appropriate graph. Explain your reasoning. (Note that the x- and y-axes are broken.)

(a) $y = 0.22x - 7.5$ (b) $y = -0.35x + 11.5$

(c) $y = 0.09x + 19.8$ (d) $y = -1.29x + 89.8$

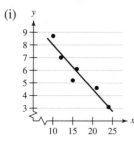

(i)

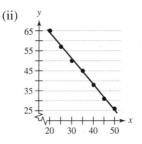

(ii)

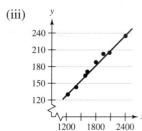

(iii)

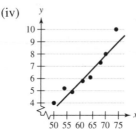

(iv)

Solution

(a) Matches (iv) because the slope in (iv) is approximately 0.22.

(b) Matches (i) because the slope in (i) is approximately -0.35.

(c) Matches (iii) because the slope in (iii) is approximately 0.09.

(d) Matches (ii) because the slope in (ii) is approximately -1.29.

Suggested Homework Assignment

Pages 953–954: 1, 7, 11, 27, 29.

Section 13.10 Lagrange Multipliers

Section Comments

13.10 Lagrange Multipliers—Understand the Method of Lagrange Multipliers. Use Lagrange multipliers to solve constrained optimization problems. Use the Method of Lagrange Multipliers with two constraints.

Teaching Tips

Begin the lesson by talking about the fact that many optimization problems have restrictions or constraints on values as outlined in the text.

In order to solve extrema problems using Lagrange multipliers, students need to solve simultaneous equations. Students may benefit from a quick review of Sections 7.2 and 7.3 of *Precalculus*, 10th edition, by Larson.

We suggest the same sample problem as outlined in Section 13.9 to review the following concepts:

- Lagrange multipliers

- Theorem 13.19

- Method of Lagrange Multipliers

166

Proceed to ask the class:

(a) Determine whether Lagrange multipliers can be used to find the dimensions of the rectangular package of largest volume that may be sent. Explain your reasoning.

(b) If Lagrange multipliers can be used, find the dimensions. Compare your answer that was worked out with the class when this question was first asked in Section 13.9.

Go over the concepts listed above and then the solution. Note that the dimensions are the same as those found in Section 13.9.

Solution

(a) Yes. Lagrange multipliers can be used.

(b) Maximize $V(x, y, z) = xyz$ subject to the constraint $x + 2y + 2z = 108$.

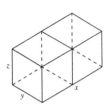

$$\left.\begin{array}{l} yz = \lambda \\ xz = 2\lambda \\ xy = 2\lambda \end{array}\right\} y = z \text{ and } x = 2y$$

$$x + 2y + 2z = 108 \implies 6y = 108, y = 18$$

$$x = 36, y = z = 18$$

Volume is maximum when the dimensions are $36 \times 18 \times 18$ inches.

How Do You See It? Exercise

Page 963, Exercise 40 The graphs show the constraint and several level curves of the objective function. Use the graph to approximate the indicated extrema.

(a) Maximize: $z = xy$
   Constraint: $2x + y = 4$

(b) Minimize: $z = x^2 + y^2$
   Constraint: $x + y - 4 = 0$

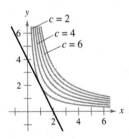

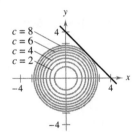

Solution

(a) $f(1, 2) = 2$

(b) $f(2, 2) = 8$

Suggested Homework Assignment

Pages 962–963: 1, 5, 7, 11, 17, 19, 23, 33, and 43.

Chapter 13 Project

Satellite Receiving Dish

Some satellite receiving dishes have the shape of a circular paraboloid. This shape allows the dish to receive signals whose strength is only a few billionths of a watt. To model a circular paraboloid, you can modify the elliptic paraboloid formula described in Section 11.6.

$$z = \frac{x^2}{a^2} + \frac{y^2}{a^2} \qquad \text{Circular paraboloid}$$

For this model, the paraboloid opens up and has its vertex at the origin. For a satellite dish, the axis of the paraboloid should pass through the satellite so that all incoming signals are parallel to the paraboloid's axis. When incoming rays strike the surface of the paraboloid at a point P, they reflect at the same angle as they would if they were reflecting off a plane that was tangent to the surface at point P, as shown in the figure on the left. All parabolas have a special reflective property. One way to describe the property is to say that *all incoming rays that are parallel to the axis of the parabola reflect directly through the focus of the parabola,* as shown in the figure on the right.

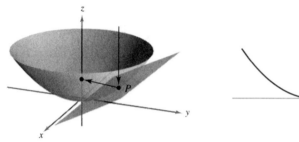
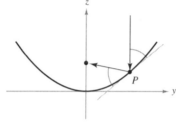

Exercises

1. You are designing a satellite receiving dish. At what point should you place the receiver? Explain your reasoning.

2. Other than satellite receiving dishes, what other common objects use the reflective property of parabolas in their design?

3. Consider the circular paraboloid given by

   $$z = x^2 + y^2$$

   and the point $P(1, 1, 2)$ on this surface. You can characterize the tangent plane to the surface at this point by saying that it is the only plane whose intersection with the paraboloid consists of the single point P. Find an equation for this tangent plane. Explain your strategy.

4. Does it make sense to talk about the "slope" of the tangent plane in Exercise 3? If so, what is the slope of this plane? How might you use differentiation to discover the slope of this plane?

5. Determine an equation of the form

   $$z = \frac{x^2}{a^2} + \frac{y^2}{a^2}$$

   for a satellite dish that has a radius of 10 feet and a depth of 3.5 feet. What is the domain and range of the equation?

168

Chapter 14 Multiple Integration

Chapter Comments

The most difficult part of multiple integration for students is often setting up the limits. Go slowly and carefully over this *every time*. Point out that the variable of integration cannot appear in either limit of integration and that the outside limits must be constant with respect to *all* variables. It is important to stress early that the order of integration does not affect the value of the integral (Example 5 on page 974). However, very often it does affect the difficulty of the problem (Example 4 on page 984). Sketching the region is a necessary part of making the decision on the order of integration.

Because polar coordinates were already covered in Chapter 10, Section 14.3 should be easy for your students, so quickly move through it.

You may have to choose which of the applications in Sections 14.4 and 14.5 that you want to discuss because you probably will not have enough time for all of them. Surface area problems are often easier when done in polar coordinates.

The problems involving triple integrals in Section 14.6 are lengthy. However, take the time to carefully set these up and work them out in detail. Encourage your students to consider the different orders of integration, looking for the simplest method of solving the problem.

Cylindrical and spherical coordinates, Section 14.7, are worth discussing well since many multiple integral problems are easier done in these coordinate systems rather than in rectangular coordinates.

The Jacobian is discussed in Section 14.8. Example 1 shows why the extra factor appears when area is calculated in polar coordinates. Be sure to assign Exercise 39, which asks for the Jacobian for the change of variables from rectangular coordinates to spherical coordinates.

Section 14.1 Iterated Integrals and Area in the Plane

Section Comments

14.1   **Iterated Integrals and Area in the Plane**—Evaluate an iterated integral. Use an iterated integral to find the area of a plane region.

Teaching Tips

Begin this lesson with the opening example in the text by finding $f(x, y) = \int f_x(x, y)\, dx = \int 2xy\, dx$ by holding y constant. As in finding partial derivatives where you are differentiating with respect to a certain variable and holding all other variables constant, you are performing the same concept with integrating with respect to a variable and holding other variables constant.

Stress the importance of Example 5, paying particular attention to setting up the double integral in two ways: by using horizontal rectangles and by using vertical rectangles. This will prove to be important for triple integration.

We suggest Exercise 69 to review the following concepts:

- Evaluating an iterated integral

- Finding the area of a plane region

- Comparing different orders of integration

How Do You See It? Exercise

Page 977, Exercise 70 Use each order of integration to write an iterated integral that represents the area of the region R (see figure).

(a) Area $= \iint dx\,dy$ (b) Area $= \iint dy\,dx$

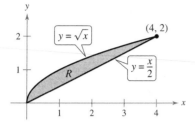

Solution

(a) $A = \displaystyle\int_0^2 \int_{y^2}^{2y} dx\,dy = \int_0^2 \Big[x\Big]_{y^2}^{2y} dy = \int_0^2 (2y - y^2)\,dy = \left[y^2 - \frac{y^3}{3}\right]_0^2 = 4 - \frac{8}{3} = \frac{4}{3}$

(b) $A = \displaystyle\int_0^4 \int_{x/2}^{\sqrt{x}} dy\,dx = \int_0^4 \Big[y\Big]_{x/2}^{\sqrt{x}} dx = \int_0^4 \left(\sqrt{x} - \frac{x}{2}\right) dx$

$\qquad = \left[\frac{2}{3}x^{3/2} - \frac{x^2}{4}\right]_0^4 = \frac{16}{3} - 4 = \frac{4}{3}$

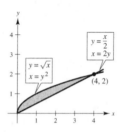

     Integrals (a) and (b) are the same.

Suggested Homework Assignment

Pages 976–977: 1, 5, 11–27 odd, 33–65 odd, and 79.

Section 14.2 Double Integrals and Volume

Section Comments

14.2   **Double Integrals and Volume**—Use a double integral to represent the volume of a solid region. Use properties of double integrals. Evaluate a double integral as an iterated integral. Find the average value of a function over a region.

Teaching Tips

Begin this lesson by giving a *brief* review of single-variable integration and Riemann sums. Transition into double integration and how these concepts will now be used.

Use Figures 14.8–14.11 to illustrate that you are now taking sample rectangular prisms to approximate the area under a surface.

You may want to start by finding $\displaystyle\iint_R 2x + 5\,dA$, where R is given by $0 \le x \le 1, 0 \le y \le 1$. You can use this problem to illustrate the sample rectangular prisms.

On page 981, we return to finding the volume of a tetrahedron. Show students that when you change what you will integrate with respect to first will not change the volume. This will be a preview of Fubini's Theorem.

Be sure to cover Examples 3–6 or similar examples.

We suggest the sample problem below to review the following concepts:

- Comparing different orders of integration

- Determining which order of integration is more convenient

The following iterated integrals represent the solution to the same problem. Which iterated integral is easier to evaluate? Explain your reasoning.

$$\int_0^4 \int_{x/2}^2 \sin y^2 \, dy \, dx = \int_0^2 \int_0^{2y} \sin y^2 \, dx \, dy$$

While some double integrals can be solved with either order of integration with comparable difficulty, others cannot. This exercise presents a case where one of the integrals does not have an elementary antiderivation (see solution). You can extend this exercise by asking students to evaluate both integrals numerically using a computer algebra system. (The answer is approximately 1.6536.)

Solution

The second is integrable. The first contains $\int \sin y^2 \, dy$, which does not have an elementary antiderivation.

How Do You See It? Exercise

Page 989, Exercise 68 The figure below shows Erie County, New York. Let $f(x, y)$ represent the total annual snowfall at the point (x, y) in the county, where R is the county. Interpret each of the following.

(a) $\displaystyle\int_R\!\!\int f(x, y) \, dA$ 　　(b) $\dfrac{\int_R\!\int f(x, y) \, dA}{\int_R\!\int dA}$

Solution

(a) $\displaystyle\int_R\!\!\int f(x, y) \, dA$ represents the total annual snowfall in Erie County.

(b) $\dfrac{\int_R\!\int f(x, y) \, dA}{\int_R\!\int dA}$ represents the average amount of snowfall at any point (x, y).

Suggested Homework Assignment

Pages 987–989: 1, 7–25 odd, 29–39 odd, 45–49 odd, 55, and 69.

Section 14.3 Change of Variables: Polar Coordinates

Section Comments

14.3   Change of Variables: Polar Coordinates—Write and evaluate double integrals in polar coordinates.

Teaching Tips

Briefly review polar coordinates with students as was discussed in Section 10.4. You may want to start the lesson by using the graphs in Figure 14.23 to review how polar coordinates can be used to describe each region.

Start the lesson by introducing Theorem 14.3 and then asking students how to convert
$$\int_{-1}^{1}\int_{-\sqrt{1-y^2}}^{\sqrt{1-y^2}} (x^2 + y^2)\, dx\, dy$$ into polar coordinates.

Be sure to carefully work out Examples 2–5 in the text.

We suggest the sample problem below to review the following concepts:

- Writing double integrals in polar coordinates

- Theorem 14.3

Without performing any calculations, identify the double integral that represents the integral of $f(x) = x^2 + y^2$ over a circle of radius 4. Explain your reasoning.

(a) $\displaystyle\int_{0}^{2\pi}\int_{0}^{4} r^2\, dr\, d\theta$
   (b) $\displaystyle\int_{0}^{4}\int_{0}^{2\pi} r^3\, dr\, d\theta$

(c) $\displaystyle\int_{0}^{2\pi}\int_{0}^{4} r^3\, dr\, d\theta$
   (d) $\displaystyle\int_{0}^{2\pi}\int_{-4}^{4} r^3\, dr\, d\theta$

Review Theorem 14.3. Note that the polar boundaries are $0 \le r \le 4$ and $0 \le \theta \le 2\pi$, as shown in the figure below.

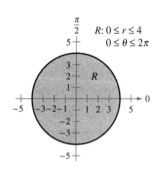

Furthermore, $x^2 + y^2 = r^2$. So, choose (c). If you choose to evaluate the integral, the answer is 128π.

Solution

$0 \le r \le 4, 0 \le \theta \le 2\pi, x^2 + y^2 = r^2$

Answer is (c).

Page 997, Exercise 56 Each figure shows a region of integration for the double integral $\int_R \int f(x, y)\, dA$. For each region, state whether horizontal representative elements, vertical representative elements, or polar sectors would yield the easiest method for obtaining the limits of integration. Explain your reasoning.

(a) 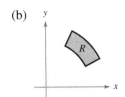 (b) 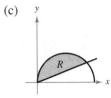 (c)

Solution

(a) Horizontal or polar representative elements

(b) Polar representative element

(c) Vertical or polar

Suggested Homework Assignment

Pages 995–997: 1, 3, 5–51 odd, and 61.

Section 14.4 Center of Mass and Moments of Inertia

Section Comments

14.4 **Center of Mass and Moments of Inertia**—Find the mass of a planar lamina using a double integral. Find the center of mass of a planar lamina using double integrals. Find moments of inertia using double integrals.

Teaching Tips

You may wish to start the lesson by talking about—for students who have had probability and statistics—the joint probability density function and the connections to the computations of mass and the center of mass. You can make the connection that the total area of a region is the probability that some outcome will occur.

You may want to present finding the mass over the unit disk: $\rho = |x| + |y|$.

How Do You See It? Exercise

Page 1005, Exercise 48 The center of mass of the lamina of constant density shown in the figure is $\left(2, \frac{8}{5}\right)$. Make a conjecture about how the center of mass $(\bar{x}, \bar{y})$ changes for each given nonconstant density $\rho(x, y)$. Explain. (Make your conjecture without performing any calculations.)

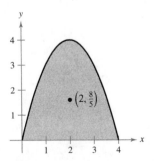

(a) $\rho(x, y) = ky$

(b) $\rho(x, y) = k|2 - x|$

(c) $\rho(x, y) = kxy$

(d) $\rho(x, y) = k(4 - x)(4 - y)$

Solution

(a) $\rho(x, y) = ky$

$\bar{y}$ will increase.

(b) $\rho(x, y) = k|2 - x|$

$\bar{y}$ will decrease.

(c) $\rho(x, y) = kxy$

Both $\bar{x}$ and $\bar{y}$ will increase.

(d) $\rho(x, y) = k(4 - x)(4 - y)$

Both $\bar{x}$ and $\bar{y}$ will increase.

Suggested Homework Assignment

Pages 1004–1005: 1, 5, 9, 15, 21, 27, 33, and 37.

Section 14.5 Surface Area

Section Comments

14.5   **Surface Area**—Use a double integral to find the area of a surface.

Teaching Tips

We suggest Exercise 33 to review the following concepts:

- Definition of surface area

- Analyzing the surface area of a function

- Comparing the surface area of a function to the area of the region of integration R

Review pages 1006 and 1007. Then go over the solution. Note from the formula for surface area on page 1007 that the least value of the radical is 1. In this case, the surface area is the area of R.

Solution

(a) Yes. For example, let R be the square given by

$0 \le x \le 1, 0 \le y \le 1,$

and S the square parallel to R given by

$0 \le x \le 1, 0 \le y \le 1, z = 1.$

(b) Yes. Let R be the region in part (a) and S the surface given by $f(x, y) = xy$.

(c) No.

How Do You See It? Exercise

Page 1011, Exercise 32 Consider the surface $f(x, y) = x^2 + y^2$ (see figure) and the surface area of f that lies above each region R. Without integrating, order the surface areas from least to greatest. Explain.

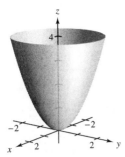

(a) R: rectangle with vertices $(0, 0)$, $(2, 0)$, $(2, 2)$, $(0, 2)$

(b) R: triangle with vertices $(0, 0)$, $(2, 0)$, $(0, 2)$

(c) $R = \{(x, y): x^2 + y^2 \leq 4,$ first quadrant only$\}$

Solution

$f(x, y) = x^2 + y^2$ is a paraboloid opening upward. Using the figure below, you see that the surface areas satisfy:

(b) < (c) < (a)

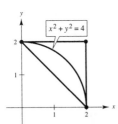

Suggested Homework Assignment

Page 1011: 1, 7, 11, 17, 19, 21, 25, and 29.

Section 14.6 Triple Integrals and Applications

Section Comments

14.6   **Triple Integrals and Applications**—Use a triple integral to find the volume of a solid region. Find the center of mass and moments of inertia of a solid region.

Teaching Tips

Begin the lesson by referring back to the concepts of area and how to find the area under a curve using a single integral, and how to find the volume under a surface using a double integral.

You may want to start out by presenting the simplest case, where the function f is defined on a rectangular box:

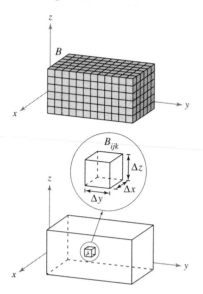

As before, you can form a Riemann sum as $\sum_{i=1}^{l} \sum_{j=1}^{m} \sum_{k=1}^{n} f(x_{ijk}^*, y_{ijk}^*, z_{ijk}^*) \, \Delta V$, where the sample point $(x_{ijk}^*, y_{ijk}^*, z_{ijk}^*)$ is in B_{ijk}.

If you have any region, Q, and if you move the bottom surface of Q to $z = f(x, y)$, then the volume of s is $V(Q) = \iiint_Q f(x, y, z) \, dV$.

Be sure to work out Example 2 and use a computer algebra system to illustrate the volume.

Stress to students that there are six different ways triple integrals can be written to lead to the volume. Present the tetrahedron $z = 1 - x - y$ and write out the six possible ways students can set up the triple integral to find the volume. The key idea is to take the shape of one side of the tetrahedron and "smash" it down to either the xy-, yz-, or xz-plane and find the sample rectangles.

You also may wish to give students a more challenging problem where one side of a three-dimensional figure is smashed down to one of the planes, resulting in splitting the integrals into two cases. For example, the figure below shows the region of integration for

$$\int_0^1 \int_0^{1-x^2} \int_0^{1-x} f(x, y, z) \, dy \, dz \, dx.$$

Have students rewrite the integral as an equivalent iterated integral in the five other orders.

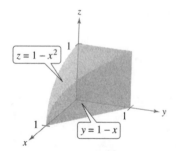

How Do You See It? Exercise

Page 1023, Exercise 70 Consider two solids of equal weight, as shown below.

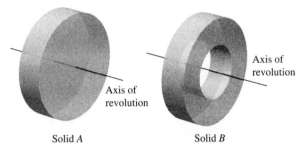

Solid A   Solid B

(a) Because the solids have the same weight, which has the greater density? Explain.

(b) Which solid has the greater moment of inertia? Explain.

(c) The solids are rolled down an inclined plane. They are started at the same time and at the same height. Which will reach the bottom first? Explain.

Solution

(a) Solid B has the greater density. Solid B has less volume, but equal weight, than solid A.

(b) Solid B has the greater moment of inertia.

(c) Solid A will reach the bottom first. Solid B has a greater resistance to rotational motion.

Suggested Homework Assignment

Pages 1021–1023: 1, 3, 7, 9, 15, 17, 23, 25, 29, 31, 33, 35, 37, 43, 53, 59, and 63.

Section 14.7 Triple Integrals in Other Coordinates

Section Comments

14.7 **Triple Integrals in Other Coordinates**—Write and evaluate a triple integral in cylindrical coordinates. Write and evaluate a triple integral in spherical coordinates.

Teaching Tips

We suggest the sample problem below to review the following concepts:

- Writing a triple integral in cylindrical coordinates

- Writing a triple integral in spherical coordinates

Convert the integral from rectangular coordinates to (a) cylindrical coordinates and (b) spherical coordinates. Without using a graphing utility, which integral appears to be the simplest to evaluate? Why?

$$\int_0^a \int_0^{\sqrt{a^2-x^2}} \int_0^{\sqrt{a^2-x^2-y^2}} \sqrt{x^2 + y^2 + z^2}\, dz\, dy\, dx$$

Many multiple integral problems are far easier done in cylindrical or spherical coordinates rather than in rectangular coordinates. Go over the method of converting from rectangular coordinates to cylindrical and spherical coordinates. Then go over the solution. Note that the integral in spherical coordinates appears to be easier to evaluate because the limits are all constants.

Solution

(a) $\displaystyle\int_0^{\pi/2}\int_0^a\int_0^{\sqrt{a^2-r^2}}\sqrt{r^2+z^2}\,r\,dz\,dr\,d\theta$ (b) $\displaystyle\int_0^{\pi/2}\int_0^{\pi/2}\int_0^a \rho^3\sin\phi\,d\rho\,d\phi\,d\theta$

Integral (b) appears simpler. The limits of integration are all constants.

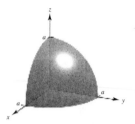

How Do You See It? Exercise

Page 1030, Exercise 46 The solid is bounded below by the upper nappe of a cone and above by a sphere (see figure). Would it be easier to use cylindrical coordinates or spherical coordinates to find the volume of the solid? Explain.

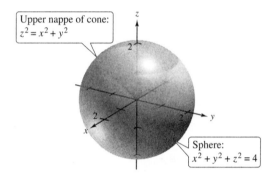

Solution

Spherical coordinates; Triple integrals involving spheres and cones are often easier to evaluate by converting to spherical coordinates.

Suggested Homework Assignment

Pages 1029–1030: 1, 7, 9, 13, 15, 19, 21, 31, and 41–43 odd.

Section 14.8 Change of Variables: Jacobians

Section Comments

14.8 Change of Variables: Jacobians—Understand the concept of a Jacobian. Use a Jacobian to change variables in a double integral.

Teaching Tips

Begin this lesson by having students recall u-substitution of a single integral. This section introduces an additional factor of $g'(u)$. This is also true for double integrals.

When stating the definition of the Jacobian, ask students to recall how to find a 2×2 determinant. The same process will be applied for the Jacobian.

Present a problem where students have to change a rectangle, $[0, 2]$ by $[0, 2\pi]$, in the uv-plane to a disk in the xy-plane by a change of variable.

178

How Do You See It? Exercise

Page 1037, Exercise 32 The region R is transformed into a simpler region S (see figure). Which substitution can be used to make the transformation?

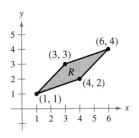

(a) $u = 3y - x, v = y - x$ (b) $u = y - x, v = 3y - x$

Solution

The transformation in (b) will make the region R into the simpler region S.

(x, y)	(u, v)
$(1, 1)$	$(0, 2)$
$(3, 3)$	$(0, 6)$
$(6, 4)$	$(-2, 6)$
$(4, 2)$	$(-2, 2)$

$$u = y - x \quad \leftrightarrow \quad x = \tfrac{1}{2}(v - 3u)$$
$$v = 3y - x \quad \leftrightarrow \quad y = \tfrac{1}{2}(v - u)$$

Suggested Homework Assignment

Pages 1036–1037: 1, 5, 11, 17, 21, 23, 25, and 29.

179

Chapter 14 Project

Hyperthermia Treatment for Tumors

Heating malignant tumors to a temperature of about 45°C can cause the tumors to regress. This treatment, known as hyperthermia, uses microwaves (or another method) to heat the tumors.

The tumor temperature during treatment is highest at the center and gradually decreases toward the edges. Regions of tissue having the same temperature, called equitherms, can be visualized as closed surfaces that are nested one inside of the other. One of the difficulties in effectively applying the hyperthermia treatment is determining the portion of the tumor heated to an effective temperature.

When normal tissue is heated, it is cooled by the dilation of blood vessels. A tumor has very few interior blood vessels and therefore is unable to take advantage of this cooling process. The problem of determining the portion of the tumor that has been heated to an effective temperature reduces to finding the ratio V_T/V, where V is the volume of the entire tumor and V_T is the volume of the portion of the tumor that is heated above temperature T.

Exercises

1. When treating a spherical tumor, a technician uses a probe to determine that the temperature has reached an appropriate level to about half the radius of the tumor. What is the ratio V_T/V? Is it $\frac{1}{2}$? Explain your reasoning.

2. Consider an ellipsoidal tumor that can be modeled by the equation

   $$\frac{x^2}{2.5} + \frac{y^2}{6.5} + \frac{z^2}{2.5} = 1.$$

   Consider a sequence of five ellipsoidal equitherms whose major and minor axes increase linearly until the fifth equitherm is the entire tumor (see figure). Write an equation for each of the five equitherms. Then find the ratio V_T/V for each of the five equitherms.

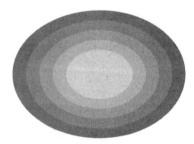

3. A certain tumor can be modeled by the wrinkled sphere given by the equation

   $$\rho = 0.5 + 0.345 \sin 8\theta \sin \phi, \quad 0 \le \theta \le 2\pi, 0 \le \phi \le \pi.$$

   (a) Explain a strategy for estimating the volume of the wrinkled sphere without using integration. Use your strategy to calculate an estimate.

   (b) Find the volume of the tumor using integration and compare the result to part (a).

4. A certain tumor can be modeled by the bumpy sphere given by the equation

   $$\rho = 0.75 + 0.35 \sin 8\theta \sin 4\phi, \quad 0 \le \theta \le 2\pi, 0 \le \phi \le \pi.$$

   Find the volume of the tumor using integration.

180

Chapter 15 Vector Analysis

Chapter Comments

Chapter 15 is divided into two parts. Sections 15.1 through 15.4 consider situations in which the integration is done over a plane region bounded by curves. Sections 15.5 through 15.8 consider integrals over regions in space bounded by surfaces. Most students find this material difficult, so go over these topics slowly and carefully. Section 15.1 contains a lot of new ideas and terminology. Take two days, if necessary, to get your students familiar with these ideas. Be sure to make it clear that the divergence of a vector field **F** is a *scalar*, while **curl F** is a *vector*.

When using parametric forms of line integrals, be sure that the parameters are chosen with *increasing* parameter values that keep the specified direction along the curve. Confusion often arises when the direction of the path is not considered (Example 7 on page 1062). Students need to understand that a line integral is independent of the parameterization of a curve C provided C is given the same orientation by all sets of parametric equations defining C. The discussion of work in Section 15.2 is an application of line integrals. Be sure to include it.

Conservative vector fields and potential functions, discussed in Section 15.3, are ideas that your students will see again in differential equations. It is important that your students know the conditions necessary for the Fundamental Theorem of Line Integrals and for path independence (Example 1 on page 1069).

Green's Theorem, in Section 15.4, is used to integrate line integrals over closed curves. Using this theorem should be fairly easy for your students if they are able to calculate the area between two curves. Be sure to note the alternative forms of Green's Theorem on page 1079.

Surface integrals, like other multiple integrals, are tedious and time consuming. However, they should be worked out in detail. Both the Divergence Theorem and Stokes's Theorem are higher dimension analogues of Green's Theorem.

Section 15.1 Vector Fields

Section Comments

15.1   **Vector Fields**—Understand the concept of a vector field. Determine whether a vector field is conservative. Find the curl of a vector field. Find the divergence of a vector field.

Teaching Tips

The most important concept to stress to students when dealing with vector fields is there are infinitely many points you can use to make the vectors. On an exam, you may want to ask students to draw vectors based on your choice of points or tails of the vectors.

Another important key idea to stress to students is that vector fields are drawn either to scale so that the lengths of the vectors are proportional to their magnitudes and the longest vectors in the field have a specified length or unscaled so that the vectors appear to be at their true magnitudes and directions.

Point out to the class that the gradient vector field is normal to all of the level curves. In addition, the gradient is the longer vector when the curves are spaced closer together.

You may want to present a real-life example of how vector fields are used. Perhaps show how NASA uses vector fields to model the wind speed and direction of a hurricane (*http://people.eecs.ku.edu/~miller/WorldWindProjects/VectorFieldVis/index.php*).

How Do You See It? Exercise

Page 1054, Exercise 68 Several representative vectors in the vector fields

$$\mathbf{F}(x, y) = \frac{x\mathbf{i} + y\mathbf{j}}{\sqrt{x^2 + y^2}} \quad \text{and} \quad \mathbf{G}(x, y) = \frac{x\mathbf{i} - y\mathbf{j}}{\sqrt{x^2 + y^2}}$$

are shown below. Match each vector field with its graph. Explain your reasoning.

(a)   (b)

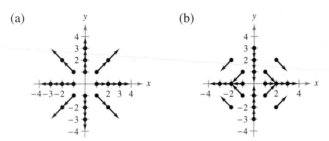

Solution

The vectors $\mathbf{F}(x, y)$ all point away from the origin. Matches (a). The vectors $\mathbf{G}(x, y)$ all point to the x-axis at a 45° degree angle. Matches (b).

Suggested Homework Assignment

Pages 1053–1054: 1, 3, 5, 7, 15, 21, 27, 33, 41, 45, 49, 51, 55, 59, and 63.

Section 15.2 Line Integrals

Section Comments

15.2   **Line Integrals**—Understand and use the concept of a piecewise smooth curve. Write and evaluate a line integral. Write and evaluate a line integral of a vector field. Write and evaluate a line integral in differential form.

Teaching Tips

Important points to cover in this lesson are the meaning of the line integral of a scalar function $f(x, y)$ along a curve C, the precise meaning of $\int P\, dx + Q\, dy$ along a curve C, vector fields, work, and the precise meaning of $\int_C \mathbf{F} \cdot d\mathbf{r}$.

A good conceptual question to ask students is given a vector field with three different curves, C_1, C_2, and C_3, arrange $\int_{C_1} \mathbf{F} \cdot d\mathbf{r}$, $\int_{C_2} \mathbf{F} \cdot d\mathbf{r}$, and $\int_{C_3} \mathbf{F} \cdot d\mathbf{r}$ from largest to smallest.

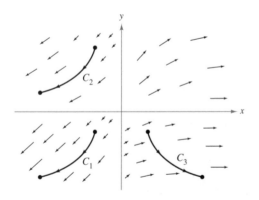

Be sure to make the connection that the line integral is similar to finding an integral of a single-variable function. Make the connection with partitioning the area under a curve to partitioning the line.

A good example to show students is given $f(x, y) = x + y$ along the curve $C = C_1 \cup C_2$, where C_1 is parametrized by $x(t) = \cos t$, $y(t) \sin t$, for $[0, \pi/2]$, and C_2 is parametrized by $x(t) = -t$, $y(t) = 1 - t$ on $[0, 1]$, find $\int_C f(x, y)\, ds$.

How Do You See It? Exercise

Page 1068, Exercise 84 For each of the following, determine whether the work done in moving an object from the first to the second point through the force field shown in the figure is positive, negative, or zero. Explain your answer. (In the figure, the circles have radii 1, 2, 3, 4, 5, and 6.)

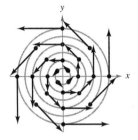

(a) From $(-3, -3)$ to $(3, 3)$

(b) From $(-3, 0)$ to $(0, 3)$

(c) From $(5, 0)$ to $(0, 3)$

Solution

(a) Work $= 0$

(b) Work is negative, because against force field.

(c) Work is positive, because with force field.

Suggested Homework Assignment

Pages 1065–1068: 1, 3, 9, 11, 15, 21, 23, 25, 31, 33, 35, 39, 41, 47, 49, 55, 59, 61, 63, 67, 85, and 87.

Section 15.3 Conservative Vector Fields and Independence of Path

Section Comments

15.3   **Conservative Vector Fields and Independence of Path**—Understand and use the Fundamental Theorem of Line Integrals. Understand the concept of independence of path. Understand the concept of conservation of energy.

Teaching Tips

The important points to stress in this section are the path independence of $\int_C \nabla f \cdot d\mathbf{r} = f(x(b), y(b)) - f(x(a), y(a))$, the equivalence of path independence to the condition that $\int_C \mathbf{F} \cdot d\mathbf{r} = 0$ for every closed curve C in the domain of $\mathbf{F}$, and the equivalence of the following on a simply connected domain:

(a) Path independence

(b) $\mathbf{F} = M\mathbf{i} + N\mathbf{j}$ being a conservative vector field ($\mathbf{F} = \nabla f$)

(c) $\dfrac{\partial M}{\partial y} = \dfrac{\partial N}{\partial x}$

Be sure to prove the Fundamental Theorem of Line Integrals as outlined in the text on page 1070.

Be sure to prove Theorem 15.6 as outlined in the text on page 1072.

We suggest Exercises 41 and 42 to review the following concepts:

- Conservative vector fields

- The Fundamental Theorem of Line Integrals (Theorem 15.5)

Review conservative vector fields (see page 1047) and Theorem 15.5 (see page 1070). These are concepts that your students will see again in differential equations.

How Do You See It? Exercise

Page 1078, Exercise 40 Consider the force field shown in the figure. To print an enlarged copy of the graph, go to *MathGraphs.com.*

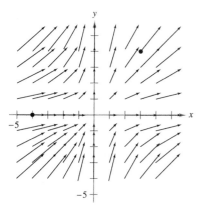

(a) Give a verbal argument that the force field is not conservative because you can identify two paths that require different amounts of work to move an object from $(-4, 0)$ to $(3, 4)$. Of the two paths, which requires the greater amount of work?

(b) Give a verbal argument that the force field is not conservative because you can find a closed curve C such that $\int_C \mathbf{F} \cdot d\mathbf{r} \neq 0$.

Solution

(a) The direct path along the line segment joining $(-4, 0)$ to $(3, 4)$ requires less work than the path going from $(-4, 0)$ to $(-4, 4)$ and then to $(3, 4)$.

(b) The closed curve given by the line segments joining $(-4, 0)$, $(-4, 4)$, $(3, 4)$, and $(-4, 0)$ satisfies $\int_C \mathbf{F} \cdot d\mathbf{r} \neq 0$.

Suggested Homework Assignment

Pages 1076–1078: 1, 3, 7, 11, 15, 21, 25, 29, 35, 43, and 45.

184

Section 15.4 Green's Theorem

Section Comments

15.4   Green's Theorem—Use Green's Theorem to evaluate a line integral. Use alternative forms of Green's Theorem.

Teaching Tips

The key concepts to address in this lesson are the statement of Green's Theorem over a region R with a boundary curve C: $\int_C M\,dx + N\,dy = \int\int_R \left(\dfrac{\partial N}{\partial x} - \dfrac{\partial M}{\partial y}\right) dA$, the extension of Green's Theorem to domains with holes, and the importance of Green's Theorem, which allows us to replace a difficult line integration problem by an easier area integration problem or vice versa.

Some suggested problems to work out with the students are:

1. Compute $\int_{C_1} \dfrac{-y}{x^2 + y^2}\,dx + \dfrac{x}{x^2 + y^2}\,dy$ by using direct computation and by using Green's Theorem where C_1 is the rectangular curve shown.

2. Evaluate $\int_C (y^2 - 2y + 2xy)\,dx + (x^2 + 3x + 2xy)\,dy$ for the closed curves C_1 and C_2.

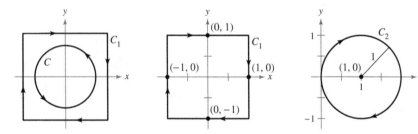

We suggest the sample problem below to review the following concepts:

- Green's Theorem

- Verifying Green's Theorem for a given path

For each given path, verify Green's Theorem by showing that $\int_C y^2\,dx + x^2\,dy = \int\int_R \left(\dfrac{\partial N}{\partial x} - \dfrac{\partial M}{\partial y}\right) dA$.

For each path, which integral is easier to evaluate? Explain.

(a) C: triangle with vertices $(0, 0)$, $(4, 0)$, $(4, 4)$

(b) C: circle given by $x^2 + y^2 = 1$

Review Green's Theorem (Theorem 15.8). Be sure to note the alternative forms of Green's Theorem on page 1079. Then go over the solution. Because students have difficulty setting up the limits of integration, go over the solution slowly and carefully. You may want to leave the evaluation of the integrals to your students. If you are pressed for time, only do part (a).

Solution

(a) $\mathbf{r}(t) = \begin{cases} t\mathbf{i}, & 0 \le t \le 4 \\ 4\mathbf{i} + (t-4)\mathbf{j}, & 4 \le t \le 8 \\ (12-t)\mathbf{i} + (12-t)\mathbf{j}, & 8 \le t \le 12 \end{cases}$

$$\int_C y^2\, dx + x^2\, dy = \int_0^4 [0\, dt + t^2(0)] + \int_4^8 [(t-4)^2(0) + 16\, dt]$$

$$+ \int_8^{12} [(12-t)^2(-dt) + (12-t)^2(-dt)]$$

$$= 0 + 64 - \frac{128}{3} = \frac{64}{3}$$

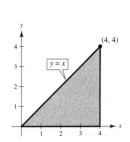

By Green's Theorem,

$$\iint_R \left(\frac{\partial N}{\partial x} - \frac{\partial M}{\partial y}\right) dA = \int_0^4 \int_0^x (2x - 2y)\, dy\, dx = \int_0^4 x^2\, dx = \frac{64}{3}.$$

(b) $\mathbf{r}(t) = \cos t\,\mathbf{i} + \sin t\,\mathbf{j}, \ 0 \le t \le 2\pi$

$$\int_C y^2\, dx + x^2\, dy = \int_0^{2\pi} [\sin^2 t(-\sin t\, dt) + \cos^2 t(\cos t\, dt)] = \int_0^{2\pi} (\cos^3 t - \sin^3 t)\, dt$$

$$= \int_0^{2\pi} [\cos t(1 - \sin^2 t) - \sin t(1 - \cos^2 t)]\, dt = \left[\sin t - \frac{\sin^3 t}{3} + \cos t - \frac{\cos^3 t}{3}\right]_0^{2\pi} = 0$$

By Green's Theorem,

$$\iint_R \left(\frac{\partial N}{\partial x} - \frac{\partial M}{\partial y}\right) dA = \int_{-1}^1 \int_{-\sqrt{1-x^2}}^{\sqrt{1-x^2}} (2x - 2y)\, dy\, dx$$

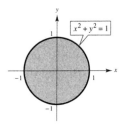

$$= \int_0^{2\pi} \int_0^1 (2r\cos\theta - 2r\sin\theta)r\, dr\, d\theta$$

$$= \frac{2}{3} \int_0^{2\pi} (\cos\theta - \sin\theta)\, d\theta = \frac{2}{3}(0) = 0.$$

How Do You See It? Exercise

Page 1086, Exercise 44 The figure shows a region R bounded by a piecewise smooth simple closed path C.

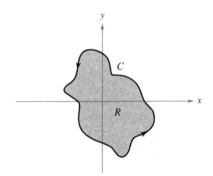

(a) Is R simply conneted? Explain.

(b) Explain why $\displaystyle\int_C f(x)\, dx + g(y)\, dy = 0$, where f and g are differentiable functions.

Solution

(a) Yes. Every simple closed curve in R encloses only points in R.

(b) $\displaystyle \int_C \mathbf{F} \cdot d\mathbf{r} = \int_C M\,dx + N\,dy = \iint_R \left(\frac{\partial N}{\partial x} - \frac{\partial M}{\partial y} \right) dA = \iint_R (0 - 0)\,dA = 0$

Suggested Homework Assignment

Pages 1085–1086: 1, 3, 7, 11, 13, 15, 17, 21, 23, 25, 27, 31, 39, 41, and 45.

Section 15.5 Parametric Surfaces

Section Comments

15.5 **Parametric Surfaces**—Understand the definition of a parametric surface, and sketch the surface. Find a set of parametric equations to represent a surface. Find a normal vector and a tangent plane to a parametric surface. Find the area of a parametric surface.

Teaching Tips

The key points to stress for this lesson are parametric surfaces and the role of gridlines in studying these surfaces, how form or symmetry of a surface helps in choosing a parametrization, differentiability and tangent planes to parametric surfaces, and the role of the area element $|\mathbf{r}_u \times \mathbf{r}_v|$ for a general parametric surface $\mathbf{r}(u, v)$.

You may want to ask students why parametrize a surface in the first place. Lead students to the answer that it helps to plot surfaces easier and to compute quantities such as surface area.

You may also want to present an example of how to determine what a surface looks like from its parametrization. Examples 1 and 2 would be good to present to the class.

You may want to present an example of how to choose a parametrization for a surface using form or symmetry. Examples 3 and 4 would be good to present to the class.

How Do You See It? Exercise

Page 1096, Exercise 48 The figures below are graphs of $\mathbf{r}(u, v) = u\mathbf{i} + \sin u \cos v\mathbf{j} + \sin u \sin v\mathbf{k}$, where $0 \le u \le \pi/2$ and $0 \le v \le 2\pi$. Match each of the four graphs with the point in space from which the surface is viewed.

(a)

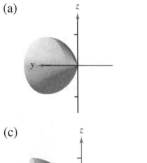

(b)

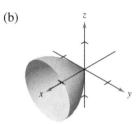

(c)

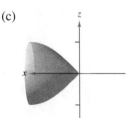

(d)

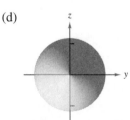

(i) $(10, 0, 0)$ (ii) $(-10, 10, 0)$

(iii) $(0, 10, 0)$ (iv) $(10, 10, 10)$

Solution

(a) From $(-10, 10, 0)$ (b) From $(10, 10, 10)$

(c) From $(0, 10, 0)$ (d) From $(10, 0, 0)$

Suggested Homework Assignment

Pages 1095–1096: 1, 3–7 odd, 11, 13, 19, 23, 25, 33, 35, 37, 41, and 45.

Section 15.6 Surface Integrals

Section Comments

15.6   **Surface Integrals**—Evaluate a surface integral as a double integral. Evaluate a surface integral for a parametric surface. Determine the orientation of a surface. Understand the concept of a flux integral.

Teaching Tips

The important points to stress to students for this section are the definition of surface integrals of a scalar function $f(x, y, z)$ as an extension of the surface area of an integral, the idea of an oriented surface with orientation given by a unit normal vector, and the surface integral of a vector field over an oriented surface.

We suggest using the sample problem below to review the following concepts:

- Identifying a normal vector to a surface

- Explaining how to find the normal component of **F** to a surface

- Evaluating a flux integral

Consider the vector field $\mathbf{F}(x, y, z) = z\mathbf{i} + x\mathbf{j} + y\mathbf{k}$ and the orientable surface S given in parametric form by $\mathbf{r}(u, v) = (u + v^2)\mathbf{i} + (u - v)\mathbf{j} + u^2\mathbf{k}, 0 \le u \le 2, -1 \le v \le 1$.

(a) Find and interpret $\mathbf{r}_u \times \mathbf{r}_v$.

(b) Find $\mathbf{F} \cdot (\mathbf{r}_u \times \mathbf{r}_v)$ as a function of u and v.

(c) Find u and v at the point $P(3, 1, 4)$.

(d) Explain how to find the normal component of **F** to the surface at P. Then find this value.

(e) Evaluate the flux integral $\int_S\int \mathbf{F} \cdot \mathbf{N} \, dS$.

Review Theorems 15.10 and 15.11. To save time, you can show students how to set up the solution to each part and leave it to them to verify the answers.

Solution

(a) $\mathbf{r}_u = \mathbf{i} + \mathbf{j} + 2u\mathbf{k}$

$\mathbf{r}_v = 2v\mathbf{i} - \mathbf{j}$

$$\mathbf{r}_u \times \mathbf{r}_v = \begin{vmatrix} \mathbf{i} & \mathbf{j} & \mathbf{k} \\ 1 & 1 & 2u \\ 2v & -1 & 0 \end{vmatrix} = 2u\mathbf{i} + 4uv\mathbf{j} - (1 + 2v)\mathbf{k}$$

$\mathbf{r}_u \times \mathbf{r}_v$ is a normal vector to the surface.

188

(b) $\mathbf{F}(u, v) = u^2\mathbf{i} + (u + v^2)\mathbf{j} + (u - v)\mathbf{k}$

$\mathbf{F} \cdot (\mathbf{r}_u \times \mathbf{r}_v) = 2u^3 + 4uv(u + v^2) - (u - v)(1 + 2v)$

$$= 2u^3 + 4u^2v + 4uv^3 + v - u + 2v^2 - 2uv$$

(c) $\left. \begin{array}{l} x = 3 = u + v^2 \\ y = 1 = u - v \\ z = 4 = u^2 \end{array} \right\} \begin{array}{l} u = 2 \\ v = 1 \end{array} \quad (u = -2 \text{ not in domain})$

(d) Calculate $\mathbf{F} \cdot \dfrac{\mathbf{r}_u \times \mathbf{r}_v}{\|\mathbf{r}_u \times \mathbf{r}_v\|}$ at P.

$\mathbf{F}(3, 1, 4) = 4\mathbf{i} + 3\mathbf{j} + \mathbf{k}$

$(\mathbf{r}_u \times \mathbf{r}_v)(2, 1) = 4\mathbf{i} + 8\mathbf{j} - 3\mathbf{k}$

$\|\mathbf{r}_u \times \mathbf{r}_v\| = \sqrt{89}$

$\mathbf{F} \cdot \dfrac{\mathbf{r}_u \times \mathbf{r}_v}{\|\mathbf{r}_u \times \mathbf{r}_v\|} = \dfrac{1}{\sqrt{89}}(16 + 24 - 3) = \dfrac{37}{\sqrt{89}} = \dfrac{37\sqrt{89}}{89}$

(e) $\displaystyle\iint_S \mathbf{F} \cdot \mathbf{N} \, dS = \iint_R \mathbf{F} \cdot (\mathbf{r}_u \times \mathbf{r}_v) \, dA$

$$= \int_{-1}^{1}\int_{0}^{2} (2u^3 + 4u^2v + 4uv^3 + v - u + 2v^2 - 2uv) \, du \, dv$$

$$= \int_{-1}^{1} \left(8v^3 + 4v^2 + \frac{26v}{3} + 6 \right) dv = \frac{44}{3}$$

How Do You See It? Exercise

Page 1109, Exercise 42 Is the surface shown in the figure orientable? Explain why or why not.

Double twist

Solution

The surface is orientable because it has two distinct sides.

Suggested Homework Assignment

Pages 1108–1109: 1, 3, 7, 9, 13, 17, 21, 23, 25, 29, and 31.

Section 15.7 Divergence Theorem

Section Comments

15.7   **Divergence Theorem**—Understand and use the Divergence Theorem. Use the
        Divergence Theorem to calculate flux.

Teaching Tips

The key points to stress for this lesson are the definition of curl and that curl $\mathbf{F} = \nabla \times \mathbf{F}$, if $\mathbf{F}$ has
continuous partial derivatives; $\mathbf{F}$ is conservative if and only if curl $\mathbf{F} = 0$; and the definition of
divergence, div $\mathbf{F} = \nabla \cdot \mathbf{F}$.

We suggest the sample problem below to review the following concepts:

- Divergence Theorem

- Using a surface integral and a triple integral to verify the Divergence Theorem for a given
  problem

Let $\mathbf{F}(x, y, z) = x\mathbf{i} + y\mathbf{j} + z\mathbf{k}$ and let S be the cube bounded by the planes $x = 0$, $x = 1$, $y = 0$,
$y = 1$, $z = 0$, and $z = 1$. Verify the Divergence Theorem by evaluating $\int_S \int \mathbf{F} \cdot \mathbf{N} \, dS$ as a surface
integral and as a triple integral.

Go over the Divergence Theorem (Theorem 15.12). You may also want to review evaluating a
surface integral (Theorem 15.10) and evaluating a triple integral (Section 14.6).

Solution

$\mathbf{F}(x, y, z) = x\mathbf{i} + y\mathbf{j} + z\mathbf{k}$

Divergence Theorem: div $\mathbf{F} = 1 + 1 + 1 = 3$

$$\iiint\limits_{Q} 3 \, dV = 3(\text{Volume of cube}) = 3$$

Surface Integral: There are six surfaces.

$x = 0$: $\mathbf{N} = -\mathbf{i}$, $\mathbf{F} \cdot \mathbf{N} = -x$, $\displaystyle\int_{S_1}\int 0 \, dS = 0$

$x = 1$: $\mathbf{N} = \mathbf{i}$, $\mathbf{F} \cdot \mathbf{N} = x$, $\displaystyle\int_{S_2}\int 1 \, dS = 1$

$y = 0$: $\mathbf{N} = -\mathbf{j}$, $\mathbf{F} \cdot \mathbf{N} = -y$, $\displaystyle\int_{S_3}\int 0 \, dS = 0$

$y = 1$: $\mathbf{N} = \mathbf{j}$, $\mathbf{F} \cdot \mathbf{N} = y$, $\displaystyle\int_{S_4}\int 1 \, dS = 1$

$z = 0$: $\mathbf{N} = -\mathbf{k}$, $\mathbf{F} \cdot \mathbf{N} = -z$, $\displaystyle\int_{S_5}\int 0 \, dS = 0$

$z = 1$: $\mathbf{N} = \mathbf{k}$, $\mathbf{F} \cdot \mathbf{N} = z$, $\displaystyle\int_{S_6}\int 1 \, dS = 1$

So, $\displaystyle\int_S\int \mathbf{F} \cdot \mathbf{N} \, dS = 1 + 1 + 1 = 3$.

How Do You See It? Exercise

Page 1117, Exercise 26 The graph of a vector field **F** is shown. Does the graph suggest that the divergence of **F** at P is positive, negative, or zero?

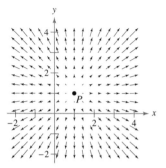

Solution

At P, the divergence is positive.

Suggested Homework Assignment

Pages 1116–1117: 1, 3, 7, 13, 17, 19, 23, and 29.

Section 15.8 Stokes's Theorem

Section Comments

15.8 Stokes's Theorem—Understand and use Stokes's Theorem. Use curl to analyze the motion of a rotating liquid.

Teaching Tips

The key ideas to point out to students in this lesson are the statements of Stokes's Theorem and the connection between the curl and the calculation of a velocity field.

Ask students if it is possible for a closed oriented curve C to be the boundary of more than one smooth oriented surface. Lead students to the answer that this is always the case.

We suggest the sample problem below to review the following concept:

- Stokes's Theorem

Verify Stokes's Theorem for each given vector field and upward-oriented surface. Is the line integral or the double integral easier to set up? To evaluate? Explain.

(a) $\mathbf{F}(x, y, z) = e^{y+z}\mathbf{i}$

   C: square with vertices $(0, 0, 0)$, $(1, 0, 0)$, $(1, 1, 0)$, $(0, 1, 0)$

(b) $\mathbf{F}(x, y, z) = z^2\mathbf{i} + x^2\mathbf{j} + y^2\mathbf{k}$

   S: the portion of the paraboloid $z = x^2 + y^2$ that lies below the plane $z = 4$

Review Stokes's Theorem (Theorem 15.13). Because students have difficulty setting up the limits of integration, go over the solution slowly and carefully. You may want to leave the evaluation of the integrals to your students. If you are pressed for time, only do part (a).

191

Solution

(a) $\mathbf{F}(x, y, z) = e^{y+z}\mathbf{i}$

From the figure you have

$C_1: r_1(t) = t\mathbf{i}, \qquad\qquad 0 \le t \le 1, \quad \mathbf{r}_1' = \mathbf{i}$

$C_2: r_2(t) = \mathbf{i} + t\mathbf{j}, \qquad\quad 0 \le t \le 1, \quad \mathbf{r}_2' = \mathbf{j}$

$C_3: r_3(t) = (1 - t)\mathbf{i} + \mathbf{j}, \quad 0 \le t \le 1, \quad \mathbf{r}_3' = -\mathbf{i}$

$C_4: r_4(t) = (1 - t)\mathbf{j}, \qquad\quad 0 \le t \le 1, \quad \mathbf{r}_4' = -\mathbf{j}$

$$\int_C \mathbf{F} \cdot d\mathbf{r} = \int_{C_1} \mathbf{F} \cdot \mathbf{r}_1' \, dt + \int_{C_2} \mathbf{F} \cdot \mathbf{r}_2' \, dt + \int_{C_3} \mathbf{F} \cdot \mathbf{r}_3' \, dt + \int_{C_4} \mathbf{F} \cdot \mathbf{r}_4' \, dt$$

$$= \int_0^1 e^0 \, dt + 0 + \int_0^1 -e^{1+0} \, dt + 0 = 1 - e$$

Double Integral: curl $\mathbf{F} = e^{y+z}\mathbf{j} - e^{y+z}\mathbf{k}$

$G(x, y) = z = 0, \mathbf{N} = \mathbf{k}$

$$\iint_S \text{curl } \mathbf{F} \cdot \mathbf{N} \, dS = \iint_R -e^y \, dA = \int_0^1 \int_0^1 -e^y \, dx \, dy = \int_0^1 -e^y \, dy = \left[-e^y\right]_0^1 = 1 - e$$

(b) $\mathbf{F}(x, y, z) = z^2\mathbf{i} + x^2\mathbf{j} + y^2\mathbf{k}$

From the figure you have

$C: \mathbf{r}(t) = 2 \cos t\mathbf{i} + 2 \sin t\mathbf{j} + 4\mathbf{k}, \quad 0 \le t \le 2\pi.$

$$\int_C \mathbf{F} \cdot d\mathbf{r} = \int_C M \, dx + N \, dy + P \, dz = \int_0^{2\pi} \left[16(-2 \sin t) + (4 \cos^2 t)(2 \cos t) + 0\right] dt$$

$$= \int_0^{2\pi} \left[-32 \sin t + 8 \cos^3 t\right] dt = 0$$

Double Integral: curl $\mathbf{F} = 2y\mathbf{i} + 2z\mathbf{j} + 2x\mathbf{k}$

$z = g(x, y) = x^2 + y^2, g_x = 2x, g_y = 2y$

$$\iint_S \text{curl } \mathbf{F} \cdot \mathbf{N} \, dS = \iint_R (2y\mathbf{i} + 2z\mathbf{j} + 2x\mathbf{k}) \cdot (-2x\mathbf{i} - 2y\mathbf{j} + \mathbf{k}) \, dA$$

$$= \iint_R \left[-4xy - 4y(x^2 + y^2) + 2x\right] dA$$

$$= \int_0^{2\pi} \int_0^2 \left[-4r \sin\theta r \cos\theta - 4r \sin\theta(r^2) - 2r \cos\theta\right] r \, dr \, d\theta$$

$$= \int_0^{2\pi} \left[\left[-16 \sin\theta - \tfrac{16}{3}\right]\cos\theta - \tfrac{128}{5} \sin\theta\right] d\theta = 0$$

How Do You See It? Exercise

Page 1123, Exercise 20 Let S_1 be the portion of the paraboloid lying above the xy-plane, and let S_2 be the hemisphere, as shown in the figures. Both surfaces are oriented upward.

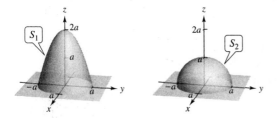

For a vector field $\mathbf{F}(x, y, z)$ with continuous partial derivatives, does

$$\int_{S_1}\int (\text{curl } \mathbf{F}) \cdot \mathbf{N} \, dS_1 = \int_{S_2}\int (\text{curl } \mathbf{F}) \cdot \mathbf{N} \, dS_2?$$

Explain your reasoning.

Solution

Yes. Both S_1 and S_2 are oriented upward and are bounded by the smooth simple closed curve $C = x^2 + y^2 = a^2$. Also, $\mathbf{F}$ is a vector field with continuous partial derivatives. So, by Stokes's Theorem

$$\int_{S_1}\int (\text{curl } \mathbf{F}) \cdot \mathbf{N} \, dS_1 = \int_C \mathbf{F} \cdot dr = \int_{S_2}\int (\text{curl } \mathbf{F}) \cdot \mathbf{N} \, dS_2.$$

Suggested Homework Assignment

Page 1123: 1, 3, 7, 11, and 13.

Chapter 15 Project

Mathematical Sculpture

Whether mathematics is seen as a science or as an art depends on one's perspective. One mathematician-sculptor, Helaman Ferguson, combines both viewpoints in a unique way. Ferguson's sculptures, which bear such names as *Cosine Wild Sphere* and *Esker Trefoil Torus*, are the concrete embodiments of mathematical concepts that incorporate ideas such as series expansions and vector fields into their creation. Some of the basic images of his work are tori and double tori, Möbius strips, and trefoil knots. One of his techniques is to use three-dimensional computer graphics to model his intended sculptures. The coordinates on the computer screen can then be used to direct the sculpting.

One example of Helaman Ferguson's work, *Umbilic Torus NC*, is shown below. This form can be written as a parametric surface using the following set of parametric equations.

$$x = \sin u \left[7 + \cos\left(\frac{u}{3} - 2v\right) + 2 \cos\left(\frac{u}{3} + v\right) \right]$$

$$y = \cos u \left[7 + \cos\left(\frac{u}{3} - 2v\right) + 2 \cos\left(\frac{u}{3} + v\right) \right]$$

$$z = \sin\left(\frac{u}{3} - 2v\right) + 2 \sin\left(\frac{u}{3} + v\right)$$

$$-\pi \le u \le \pi, \qquad -\pi \le v \le \pi$$

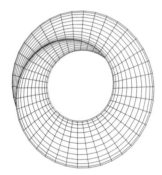

Generated by Mathematica

Mathematica rendition of *Umbilic Torus NC*

Exercises

1. Explain how the umbilic torus shown above is similar to a Möbius strip like the one shown below.

2. Use a three-dimensional computer algebra system to graph the torus. You will have to use the *parametric surface* graphing mode.

3. When viewed head-on (along the z-axis), the torus appears nearly circular. Is it possible to alter this appearance so that the shape of the torus is more like that of an elongated ellipse? If so, use a computer algebra system to graph an "elliptical" torus.

194

Chapter 16 Additional Topics in Differential Equations

Chapter Comments

One of the most difficult parts of solving differential equations is recognizing the type of equation: separable, linear, exact, and so forth. Briefly review Chapter 6 with your students. Then, with each assignment given in the chapter, add a few carefully chosen differential equations—one of each type studied thus far. Mix them up and do not indicate the method to be used. Let students decide that. Remind your students that there are many correct ways that an answer to a differential equation can be written.

Your students should recognize exact differential equations from their work in Chapter 15 on conservative vector fields and potential functions.

Sections 16.2 and 16.3 consider techniques for solving differential equations of order higher than one. For a homogeneous equation, use the techniques outlined in Section 16.2 and for nonhomogeneous equations, the method of undetermined coefficients or variation of parameters is appropriate.

Finally, Section 16.4 examines power series solutions to differential equations.

Section 16.1 Exact First-Order Equations

Section Comments

16.1   **Exact First-Order Equations**—Solve an exact differential equation. Use an integrating factor to make a differential equation exact.

Teaching Tips

If needed, *briefly* review Chapter 6 when first-order equations were first introduced.

We suggest using the sample problem below to review the following concepts:

- First-order linear differential equations (Chapter 6)

- Integrating factors (Theorem 16.2)

- Theorem 6.2

In Chapter 6, you solved the first-order linear differential equation

$$\frac{dy}{dx} + P(x)y = Q(x)$$

by using the integrating factor

$$u(x) = e^{\int P(x)\,dx}.$$

Show that you can obtain this integrating factor by using the methods of this section.

Review the definition of first-order linear differential equation (see page 432) and Theorem 16.2. Then show students how to obtain the integrating factor given in Theorem 6.2 (see page 433).

Solution

$$\frac{dy}{dx} + P(x)y = Q(x)$$

$$dy + P(x)y\,dx = Q(x)\,dx$$

$$[P(x)y - Q(x)]\,dx + dy = 0$$

$$M(x, y) = P(x)y - Q(x) \quad \text{and} \quad N(x, y) = 1$$

$$\frac{M_y(x, y) - N_x(x, y)}{N(x, y)} = \frac{\dfrac{d}{dy}[P(x)y - Q(x)] - \dfrac{d}{dx}[1]}{1}$$

$$= P(x)$$

By Theorem 16.2, $u(x) = e^{\int P(x)\,dx}$ is an integrating factor.

How Do You See It? Exercise

Page 1136, Exercise 46 The graph shows several representative curves from the family of curves tangent to a force field **F**. Which is the equation of the force field? Explain your reasoning.

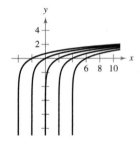

(a) $\mathbf{F}(x, y) = -\mathbf{i} + 2\mathbf{j}$ (b) $\mathbf{F}(x, y) = -3x\mathbf{i} + y\mathbf{j}$

(c) $\mathbf{F}(x, y) = e^x\mathbf{i} - \mathbf{j}$ (d) $\mathbf{F}(x, y) = 2\mathbf{i} + e^{-y}\mathbf{j}$

Solution

(d) Because at $(0, 0)$, $\mathbf{F}(0, 0) = 2\mathbf{i} + \mathbf{j}$ has slope $\frac{1}{2}$.

For (a), $\mathbf{F}(0, 0) = -\mathbf{i} + 2\mathbf{j}$ has negative slope.

For (b), $\mathbf{F}(0, 0) = \mathbf{i}$.

For (c), $\mathbf{F}(0, 0) = \mathbf{i} - \mathbf{j}$.

Suggested Homework Assignment

Pages 1135–1136: 1, 5, 9, 13, 15, 17, 25, 29, 35, 39, 55, and 57.

Section 16.2 Second-Order Homogeneous Linear Equations

Section Comments

16.2 **Second-Order Homogeneous Linear Equations**—Solve a second-order linear differential equation. Solve a higher-order linear differential equation. Use a second-order linear differential equation to solve an applied problem.

Teaching Tips

The key points to stress in this lesson are the homogeneous linear differential equation $y'' + ay' + by = 0$ and the associated characteristic equation $m^2 + am + b = 0$; the various forms of the general solution for distinct real, equal real, and complex zeros for the characteristic equation; and the unique solutions for initial value problems.

You may wish to present the solution of the initial value problem $y' + 2y = 0$, $y(0) = 1$, $y'(0) = 1$ to get $y = \cos 2x + \sin 2x$.

Present examples of many different homogeneous linear equations that have distinct real solutions, complex conjugate solutions, and repeated solutions. Examples 2 through 4 are good examples to work out with the class.

We suggest using the sample problem below to review the following concepts:

- Second-order linear differential equations

- Theorems 16.3 and 16.4

- Characteristic equation

Find all values of k for which the differential equation $y'' + 2ky' + ky = 0$ has a general solution of the indicated form.

(a) $y = C_1 e^{m_1 x} + C_2 e^{m_2 x}$

(b) $y = C_1 e^{m_1 x} + C_2 x e^{m_1 x}$

(c) $y = C_1 e^{ax} \cos \beta x + C_2 e^{ax} \sin \beta x$

Go over the definition of linear differential equation of order n (see page 1137) and note that the order of the differential equation in this example is 2. Then review Theorems 16.3 and 16.4, and characteristic equation (see page 1138). Students should recognize that parts (a)–(c) of the exercise are the solutions listed in Theorem 16.4. Write the characteristic equation and follow the solution below.

Solution

$y'' + 2ky' + ky = 0$

Characteristic equation: $m^2 + 2km + k = 0$

$$m = \frac{-2k \pm \sqrt{4k^2 - 4k}}{2} = -k + \sqrt{k^2 - 1}$$

(a) For $k < -1$, and $k > 1$, $k^2 - 1 > 0$ and there are two distinct real roots.

(b) For $k = \pm 1$, $k^2 - 1 = 0$ and the roots are repeated.

(c) For $-1 < k < 1$, the roots are complex.

How Do You See It? Exercise

Page 1144, Exercise 54 Give a geometric argument to explain why the graph cannot be a solution of the differential equation. (It is not necessary to solve the differential equation.)

(a) $y'' = y'$ (b) $y'' = -\frac{1}{2}y'$

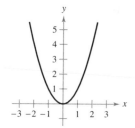 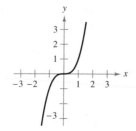

Solution

(a) y'' is always positive according to the graph (concave upward), but y' is negative when $x < 0$ (decreasing), so $y'' \neq y'$.

(b) y'' is positive for $x > 0$ (concave upward), but $-\frac{1}{2}y' < 0$ for $x > 0$ (increasing). So, $y'' \neq -\frac{1}{2}y'$.

Suggested Homework Assignment

Pages 1143–1144: 1, 3, 5, 9–35 odd, 39, 47, 49, 57, 61, 67, and 69.

Section 16.3 Second-Order Nonhomogeneous Linear Equations

Section Comments

16.3 **Second-Order Nonhomogeneous Linear Equations**—Recognize the general solution of a second-order nonhomogeneous linear differential equation. Use the method of undetermined coefficients to solve a second-order nonhomogeneous linear differential equation. Use the method of variation of parameters to solve a second-order nonhomogeneous linear differential equation.

Teaching Tips

Be sure to point out to students that every general solution of a nonhomogeneous linear equation is the sum of one particular solution and a solution to the complementary homogeneous equation. Carefully present the method of undetermined coefficients to find a particular solution and present an introduction to the method of variation of parameters.

You may wish to start by asking students when solving $3y'' + 4y' - 2y = e^{2x}$, why you should first find a solution to $3y'' + 4y' - 2y = 0$. Lead students to the answer that when added to one particular solution, the homogeneous solution gives the general solution.

Be sure to explain the reasons behind every solution of the differential equation $ay'' + by' + cy = F(x)$ can be written as $y = y_h + y_p$, where y_h is one particular solution and y_p is a solution to the complementary homogeneous equation.

In addition, you can categorize the graphs of solutions of homogeneous linear equations. $y = 0$ will always be a solution, which is *not* the case with nonhomogeneous linear equations.

We suggest using the sample problem below to review the following concepts:

- Nonhomogeneous linear differential equations

- Theorem 16.5

198

(a) Explain how, by observation, you know that a particular solution of the differential equation $y' + 3y = 12$ is $y_p = 4$.

(b) Use your explanation in part (a) to give a particular solution of the differential equation $y' + 5y = 10$.

(c) Use your explanation in part (a) to give a particular solution of the differential equation $y'' + 2y' + 2y = 8$.

Go over nonhomogeneous linear differential equations and Theorem 16.5 on page 1145. Then go over the solution.

Solution

(a) Because $y_p'' = 0$ and $3(y_p) = 3(4) = 12$

(b) $y_p = 2$

(c) $y_p = 4$

How Do You See It? Exercise

Page 1152, Exercise 36 The figure shows the particular solution of the differential equation

$$\frac{4}{32}y'' + by' + \frac{25}{2}y = 0$$

that models the oscillating motion of an object on the end of a spring and satisfies the initial conditions $y(0) = \frac{1}{2}$ and $y'(0) = -4$ for values of the resistance component b in the interval $[0, 1]$. According to the figure, is the motion damped or undamped when $b = 0$? When $b > 0$? (You do not need to solve the differential equation.)

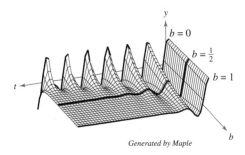

Generated by Maple

Solution

When $b = 0$, the motion is undamped. When $b > 0$, the motion is damped.

Suggested Homework Assignment

Pages 1151–1152: 1, 3, 9, 11, 19, 25, 33, and 39.

Section 16.4 Series Solutions of Differential Equations

Section Comments

16.4   Series Solutions of Differential Equations—Use a power series to solve a differential equation. Use a Taylor series to find the series solution of a differential equation.

199

Teaching Tips

The key points to stress to students in this lesson are the use of infinite series as solutions to differential equations and the method of recursion relations to determine the coefficients of a series.

You may want to *briefly* touch on the series presented in Chapter 9. For example, $\sum_{n=0}^{\infty} \frac{x^n}{n!}$.

Point out to students that the general idea of differential equations says that if you start with a differential equation $y'' + P(x)y' + Q(x)y = 0$, then there are always two linearly independent series solutions $y(x) = \sum_{n=0}^{\infty} c_n x^n$.

Make sure to work out Examples 1 through 3 in detail.

We suggest using the sample problem below to review the following concepts:

- The techniques presented in Section 16.2

- Using a Taylor series to find the series solution of a differential equation

Consider the differential equation $y' + 9y = 0$ with initial conditions $y(0) = 2$ and $y'(0) = 6$.

(a) Find the solution of the differential equation using the techniques presented in Section 16.2.

(b) Find the series solution of the differential equation.

Review Theorems 16.3 and 16.4, and characteristic equation (see Section 16.2). Then do part (a). Then go over how to use a Taylor series to find the series solution of a differential equation by doing part (b).

Solution

(a) $m^2 + 9 = 0 \implies m = \pm 3i$

$y = C_1 \cos 3x + C_2 \sin 3x$

$y(0) = 2 = C_1$

$y' = -3C_1 \sin 3x + 3C_2 \cos 3x$

$y'(0) = 6 = 3C_2 \implies C_2 = 2$

$y_p = 2 \cos 3x + 2 \sin 3x$

(b) Let $y = \sum_{n=0}^{\infty} a_n x^n$, $y' = \sum_{n=1}^{\infty} n a_n x^{n-1}$, $y'' = \sum_{n=2}^{\infty} n(n-1)a_n x^{n-2}$.

$y'' + 9y = \sum_{n=2}^{\infty} n(n-1)a_n x^{n-2} + 9 \sum_{n=0}^{\infty} a_n x^n = 0$

$\sum_{n=0}^{\infty} (n+2)(n+1)a_{n+2} x^n + 9 \sum_{n=0}^{\infty} a_n x^n = 0$

$(n+2)(n+1)a_{n+2} = -9a_n$

$a_{n+2} = \frac{-9}{(n+2)(n+1)} a_n$

For *n* even,

$$a_2 = \frac{-9}{2}a_0$$

$$a_4 = \frac{-9}{4 \cdot 3}a_2 = \frac{(-9)^2}{4!}a_0$$

$$a_6 = \frac{(-9)^3}{6!}a_0$$

and in general, $a_{2n} = \frac{(-9)^n}{(2n)!}a_0.$

For *n* odd,

$$a_3 = \frac{-9}{3 \cdot 2}a_1$$

$$a_5 = \frac{-9}{5 \cdot 4}a_3 = \frac{(-9)^2}{5!}a_1$$

$$a_7 = \frac{(-9)^3}{7!}a_1$$

and in general, $a_{2n+1} = \frac{(-9)^n}{(2n+1)!}a_1.$

So, $y = \displaystyle\sum_{n=0}^{\infty} a_n x^n = \sum_{n=0}^{\infty} a_{2n}x^{2n} + \sum_{n=0}^{\infty} a_{2n+1}x^{2n+1}$

$$= \sum_{n=0}^{\infty} \frac{(-9)^n}{(2n)!}a_0 x^{2n} + \sum_{n=0}^{\infty} \frac{(-9)^n}{(2n+1)!}a_1 x^{2n+1} = a_0 \sum_{n=0}^{\infty} \frac{(-1)^n (3x)^{2n}}{(2n)!} + a_1 \sum_{n=0}^{\infty} \frac{(-1)^n (3x)^{2n+1}}{(2n+1)!}.$$

Applying the initial conditions,

$$a_0 = a_1 = 2, \text{ and } y = 2\left[\sum_{n=0}^{\infty} \frac{(-1)^n (3x)^{2n}}{(2n)!} + \sum_{n=0}^{\infty} \frac{(-1)^n (3x)^{2n+1}}{(2n+1)!} \right].$$

How Do You See It? Exercise

Page 1156, Exercise 20 Consider the differential equation $y'' + 9y = 0$, with initial conditions $y(0) = 2$ and $y'(0) = 6$. The figure shows the graph of the solution of the differential equation and the third-degree and fifth-degree polynomial approximations of the solution. Identify each.

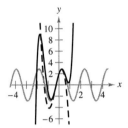

Solution

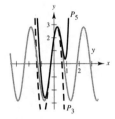

Suggested Homework Assignment

Page 1156: 1, 5, 7, 9, 13, 19, 21, and 23.

Chapter 16 Project

Velocity of a Parachutist

The fall of a parachutist is given by the second-order linear differential equation $\dfrac{w}{g}\dfrac{d^2y}{dt^2} - k\dfrac{dy}{dt} = w$,

where w is the weight of the parachutist (in pounds), y is the height (in feet) at time t (in seconds), g is the acceleration due to gravity, and k is the drag factor of the parachute.

In Exercises 1–5, a 160-pound person opens the parachute at 2000 feet and at that time, is falling at a speed of 100 feet per second. Use $k = 8$ for the drag factor of the parachute.

1. Use the information provided to write a second-order linear differential equation with initial conditions.

2. Solve the differential equation for y'.

3. Use the equation from Exercise 2 to find an equation for y.

4. Use a graphing utility to determine when the parachutist will reach the ground.

5. What is the parachutist's velocity at impact?

In Exercises 6–10, a 160-pound person opens the parachute at 1500 feet and at that time, is falling at a speed of 150 feet per second. Use $k = 8$ for the drag factor of the parachute.

6. Use the information provided to write a second-order linear differential equation with initial conditions.

7. Solve the differential equation for y'.

8. Use the equation from Exercise 7 to find an equation for y.

9. Use a graphing utility to determine when the parachutist will reach the ground.

10. What is the parachutist's velocity at impact?

In Exercises 11–15, a 120-pound person opens the parachute at 2000 feet and at that time, is falling at a speed of 75 feet per second. Use $k = 8$ for the drag factor of the parachute.

11. Use the information provided to write a second-order linear differential equation with initial conditions.

12. Solve the differential equation for y'.

13. Use the equation from Exercise 12 to find an equation for y.

14. Use a graphing utility to determine when the parachutist will reach the ground.

15. What is the parachutist's velocity at impact?

16. Show that the velocity of a parachutist is given by the equation $v = \dfrac{-w}{k} + Ce^{(kg/w)t}$.

17. For large values of t, what happens to the equation in Exercise 16? What does this mean in the context of the problem?